The twentieth century has seen biology come of age as a conceptual and quantitative science. Major functional phenomena rather than catalogues of animals and plants comprise the core of MODERN BIOLOGY; such heretofore seemingly unrelated fields as cytology, biochemistry, and genetics are now being unified into a common framework at the molecular level.

The purpose of this Series is to introduce the beginning student in college biology—as well as the gifted high school student and all interested readers—both to the concepts unifying the fields of biology and to the diversity of facts that give the entire field its unique texture. Each book in the Series is an introduction to one of the major foundation stones in the mosaic. Taken together, they provide an integration of the general and the comparative, the cellular and the organismic, the animal and the plant, the structural and the functional—in sum, a solid overview of the dynamic science that is MODERN BIOLOGY.

MODERN BIOLOGY SERIES

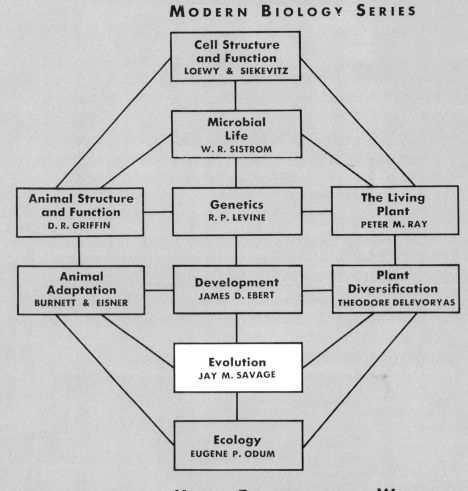

Cell Structure and Function
LOEWY & SIEKEVITZ

Microbial Life
W. R. SISTROM

Animal Structure and Function
D. R. GRIFFIN

Genetics
R. P. LEVINE

The Living Plant
PETER M. RAY

Animal Adaptation
BURNETT & EISNER

Development
JAMES D. EBERT

Plant Diversification
THEODORE DELEVORYAS

Evolution
JAY M. SAVAGE

Ecology
EUGENE P. ODUM

HOLT, RINEHART AND WINSTON

NEW YORK - CHICAGO - SAN FRANCISCO - TORONTO - LONDON

EVOLUTION

JAY M. SAVAGE

UNIVERSITY OF SOUTHERN CALIFORNIA

PREFACE

Evolution is a vast and complex subject, one that touches upon every phase of biology, from biochemistry and cell physiology to systematics and ecology. This book is written in the strong conviction that the study of evolution is fundamental to the understanding of any field of biology and forms a rich area of investigation in its own right.

No serious biologist today doubts the fact of evolution, the development of all living organisms from previously existing types under the control of evolutionary processes. However, there have been and will continue to be differences of opinion on how evolution takes place, just as there are different ideas on the exact processes involved in, for example, the formation of mountain ranges. Thus while the fact of evolution is amply clear, there are different theories regarding the significant processes that have brought about evolutionary change.

In this book we are not concerned with enumerating so-called proofs of evolution. The fact of evolution is demonstrated on every side in all fields of biology and indeed forms the basic unifying principle in the study of living systems. We do not need a listing of evidences to demonstrate the fact of evolution any more than we need to demonstrate the existence of mountain ranges. Rather, the concern here will be with what is known about the process of evolution and a survey of the several theories proposed to explain the process. In particular, I will develop the most generally accepted theory of evolution as supported by material evidences, observations, experiments, and theories of basic evolutionary forces. An understanding of the manner in which evolution takes place should provide all the evidence necessary to convince men with open minds of the reality of this phenomenon. For those requiring additional examples and greater detail two books are especially recommended: *Evolution and Genetics*, D. J. Merrell (Holt, Rinehart and Winston, 1962) and *The Meaning of Evolution*, G. G. Simpson (Yale University, 1949).

The present book is unique among discussions of evolution at the college level in its emphasis on the two crucial unsolved problems in the understanding of evolutionary processes: (1) By what means do isolating mechanisms develop to prevent genetic exchange between related populations of organisms and lead to the origin of species? (2) What processes are responsible for the origin of major evolutionary changes above the species level? The ultimate solution of these problems is left, hopefully, to readers of this book.

Appreciation is due Professors David J. Merrell and E. Peter Volpe, who have offered useful suggestions and advice. Richard E. Casey aided in the preparation of the preliminary sketches for the line drawings and Bertha M. Jensen prepared all the manuscript drafts; to them my thanks. Finally I wish to acknowledge my debt to my teachers at Stanford University, especially Rolf L. Bolin, Gordon F. Ferris, George S. Myers, and David G. Regnery, who introduced me to the complexities of evolution, and to my graduate students at the University of Southern California, who encourage me to delve deeper into the subject each day.

J.M.S.

La Mirada, California
February, 1963

CONTENTS

PART I

INTRODUCTION

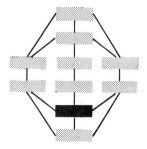

CHAPTER ONE

EVOLUTION AND LIFE

Two underlying themes seem to characterize all life: *diversity* and *unity*. Diversity is exemplified by the approximately two million different species of organisms living today and the many millions of species that formerly existed on the earth and are now extinct. Diversity in every conceivable feature associated with life activities is found in this vast and almost overwhelming array of life, which ranges from simple viruses through unicellular organisms to such complex but diverse entities as whales and palm trees. Diversity is an obvious feature of life. Less apparent but equally typical of living organisms is unity in basic characteristics. Unity in the living world is not so obvious to the casual observer as diversity but it is recognized by the fact that most of us see, dimly, a common similarity in all life. A full realization of the unity of life in terms of the fundamental characteristics of reproduction and energy transformation and utilization only recently has been developed, and it constitutes one of the major triumphs of science in the twentieth century. Biological systems, no matter how complex, all exhibit a basic unity of fundamental life processes. Overlying the unifying elements are the features that give rise to diversity and the distinctive mode of existence for each group of organisms.

The twin themes of diversity and unity in life have appeared to some people as antagonistic or mutually exclusive principles each incompatible with the other, and it is only through the concept of evolution that the two themes are reconciled. The degree to which diversity and unity influence biologists is clearly indicated in the *Modern Biology Series*. All of the other books in the series deal primarily with either diversity (*Microbial Life, Animal Structure and Function, Animal Adaptation, The Living Plant,* and *Plant Diversification*) or unity (*Cell Structure and Function, Genetics, Development,* and *Ecology*). Because it provides an explanation of how diversity and unity may be characteristic of living systems at the same time, the principle of evolution occupies a central unifying position within the field of biology.

The idea of evolution as the single most significant concept developed in the study of living organisms provides explanations for myriad biological processes and pervades every branch of biology from biochemistry and physiology to ecology and morphology. In addition, the concept has had a profound impact upon thinking in every field of knowledge. Essentially, the principle of evolution implies *development of an entity in the course of time through a gradual sequence of changes from a simple to a more complex state*. The idea was originally applied to the historical development of life, and the word "evolution" was first applied to this process by the English philosopher Herbert Spencer. It is now recognized that organic evolution forms a very special part of a more general evolutionary process: the development of our universe, or cosmic evolution.

The present book is restricted to analysis of that portion of cosmic evolution responsible for the unity and diversity of life. Hereafter the word evolution will be used when reference is made to organic evolution, but any phase of nonorganic evolution will be clearly denoted by an appropriate modifier. In a broad sense, biological evolution involves two different kinds of development. Each individual organism undergoes a developmental process from its time of origin until death. Every human being, for example, begins life as a single small cell, which then passes through a series of increasingly complex changes, culminating in a fully developed coordinated multicellular adult. The evolution of the individual is called *ontogeny*, and since the most rapid period of change occurs during early development, or embryogenesis, ontogenetic changes are usually studied by embryologists. Although the evolutionist is interested in ontogeny, his primary concern is with a second kind of development. We know that every group of living organisms—populations, species, genera, families, orders, classes, phyla, and kingdoms—has undergone changes through the course of time and as a result, living forms are the descendants of previously existing and rather different ancestors. The historical development of groups of organisms is referred to as *phylogeny*, and it is with phylogenetic evolution that most modern students of evolution are concerned. It is the result of phylogenetic evolution that all organisms exhibit unity in basic biological processes, since all the diverse lines of evolution are descendants of common ancestors. Diversity is a result of phylogenetic change and is superimposed upon the unity provided by common ancestry.

Obviously, living organisms are not the only entities that are the products of developmental processes. The universe in which we live is the product of a series of developmental changes, or cosmic evolution. The planet earth as we know it today is the result of historical changes or geologic evolution. The historical stages leading to the rise of human civilizations may be spoken of as cultural evolution. And we may even refer to the evolution of airplanes, automobiles, radios, telephones, and ideas, although each of these forms a special case of cultural evolution. Even though these various kinds of evolution resemble one another in having the characteristic of a sequence of developmental stages, none, because of the unique qualities of living organisms, is precisely the same as organic evolution.

THE NATURE OF LIFE

In order to appreciate fully the nature of evolution, it is necessary to consider the material basis of life. No generally applicable definition of life is possible, simply because living systems appear to be extremely complex organizations of nonliving materials, operating in accordance with the same physicochemical principles evident in the functioning of the inorganic world. Life is particularly difficult to define because it is a dynamic, continuously changing process of unimaginable complexity. This complexity is reflected in the organization of living systems as compared to nonliving ones. We know that all materials, living and nonliving, are formed of certain basic units called *atoms*. Atoms are combined in specific ways to form various kinds of *molecules*. All nonliving systems are composed of groups of one kind of molecule (substances) or of several kinds of molecules (mixtures). Living systems are mixtures of very large and complex molecules functioning together in a coordinated manner. The very largest and most complex nonliving molecules (*proteins*) approach in size and chemical activity the very smallest of living systems (*viruses*). Above the virus level, living material is usually organized into units called *cells*. These units are made up of a great many different kinds of complex molecules. Individual organisms are composed of one to a great many cells. Above the individual level are additional organizational units of increasing complexity: the *population*, the *species*, the *community*, and finally, the *ecosystem*. The spectrum of organization is illustrated in Table 1-1. It is important to recognize that just as every living thing is composed of the basic physical units—atoms and molecules—each individual organism can only exist as a part of a particular population, species, community, and ecosystem.

All living creatures are composed of a peculiar combination of nonliving substances. The chemistry of the principal constituents of protoplasm is in large part responsible for the attributes of life. The most important components of all living materials are water (H_2O) and large molecules containing carbon atoms: the carbohydrates, lipids (fats), and proteins. Proteins also share characters in common because of the presence of nitrogen and usually sulfur in their structure. In addition to these materials, complex proteinaceous catalysts, called enzymes, initiate and regulate most of the

TABLE 1-1

Spectrum of Organizational Complexity
(Each unit is made up of the units immediately below.)

	Unit	Composition
most *complex*	Ecosystem	Community and nonliving environment
	Community	Several to many interacting species
	Species	One to several genetically similar populations
	Population	Several to many genetically similar individuals
	Individual	One to many cells
	Cell	Organized living material under regulatory control of genetic materials; complex colloidal mixture of carbohydrate, lipid, and protein molecules, plus other substances in water
		Organized subcellular living material ranging in composition from a single large protein molecule to several protein molecules, containing DNA or RNA: the viruses
	Molecule	Two to many atoms
simplest	Atom	Two to many fundamental particles (protons, neutrons, electrons) bound together by energy

increasing complexity — LIVING SYSTEMS — NONLIVING SYSTEMS

chemical activities of living systems. Finally, all of the many different kinds of carbohydrates, lipids, proteins, and enzymes, and small amounts of a great many inorganic materials are organized into a colloidal mixture in the water. This physical arrangement contributes potentialities for complex chemical activity by increasing the number of interactions between the many kinds of molecules. It is apparent that all living organisms are composed of the same basic materials and units found in the nonliving world. That life is a manifestation of much greater complexity than any nonliving system is underscored when we stop to realize that even the simplest cell is composed of thousands of different kinds of molecules operating together in a coordinated fashion.

Special comment must be made concerning the extremely small organisms called viruses. These forms are little more than single large protein molecules. All are made up of one to several protein molecules containing deoxyribonucleic acid (DNA) or ribonucleic acid (RNA). Their structure is without evidence of cellular organization, and although most biologists generally regard them as microorganisms, some are inclined to dismiss them as peculiar nonliving systems. Most scientists today believe that viruses are probably bits of genetic material, equal to fragments of the chromosomes of cellular forms. Significantly, viruses resemble very closely any proposed intermediate between nonliving molecules and living material. Whatever their status, the viruses provide a demonstration of the absence of any clear-cut break in the continuum from nonliving to living systems.

The complexity of the physicochemical organization of life makes possible a number of fundamental processes that occur in a regulated, organized fashion in all living systems. The first of these features is the product of the chemical organization and enzymatic activities of living material. All life has the ability to take nonliving materials and to convert them into part of the living system. Each one of us converts the nonliving foods from his daily meals into living human being, and all other living organisms display this same capacity. Associated with this characteristic is the further ability to break down certain portions of the organism's own living substance in order to release energy for life's activities. The abilities of *conversion* and *energy production* are spoken of collectively as *autosynthesis* and are typical of all living systems from viruses to men. Viruses, however, are unique in that they display these features only when they are within the cells of some other living organism. No nonliving system exhibits the attribute of autosynthesis.

A second peculiar feature of life is its capacity for *reproduction*. Each kind of living organism is able to produce new individuals that are essentially duplicates of the parent or parents. All human beings reproduce human beings, not snakes, sunflowers, or viruses. The processes of biological reproduction are ultimately under the control of special enzymatic regulators produced by the activity of fundamental hereditary units called *genes*. The genes are self-duplicating units and are basically responsible for the self-duplicating feature of biological reproduction. The genes are currently thought to be specialized chemical molecules composed of different DNA molecules. Differences in the chemical structure of the DNA molecules are apparently translated into the production of different enzyme systems. The differences in the sum total of all enzymatic activities, especially as these regulate ontogenetic development, are responsible for the differences between various kinds of living organisms. The reason that a lion is not an oak tree lies in the fact that a lion has an enzyme control system greatly different

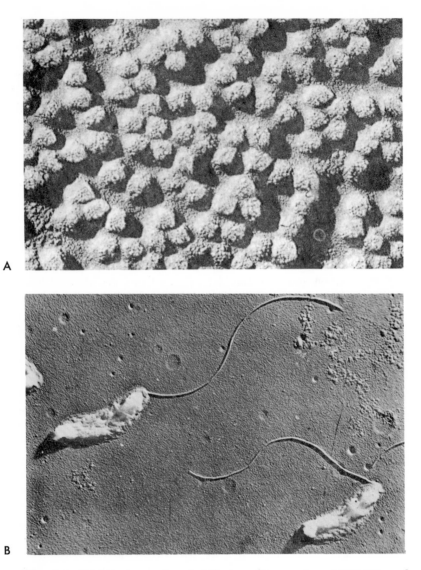

A

B

Fig. 1-1. Electronmicrographs of (A) wound-tumor virus, ×100,000, and (B) a bacterium, *Vibrio*, ×5000. (Courtesy of R. F. Bils.)

from that of an oak. The enzyme systems differ because the hereditary materials, genes, are different in the two kinds of organisms. The special kind of self-duplicating reproduction made possible by the genes is called *autocatalysis* and it is typical of all living organisms. Viruses alone among living creatures are only autocatalytic when they are within the cells of other organisms. The viruses apparently are composed primarily of proteins containing DNA or RNA, and an individual virus is essentially one to several naked genes. No nonliving system is capable of the precise autocatalytic reproduction found in living organisms.

The third major characteristic of all living systems is their capacity for regulated adjustment to a changing world. The process of change is called *adaptation*. Every living organism changes constantly to maintain life's activities under changing environmental conditions. Every organism has some capacity for immediate environmental adjustment to sudden changes in the surrounding environment. For example, if the air temperature outside a human being's body goes up, the person will make a series of adjustments, including perspiring, to maintain the body temperature at a constant level. Short-term internally regulated adaptational responses to external changes or stimuli are expressions of *irritability*. Such stimulus-response adaptations provide for maintenance of the organism in the flux of external circumstance. All organisms are, in addition, a product of long-term adaptation to a gradually changing world. Each kind of living organism is descended from ancestors who were not adapted in exactly the same way to the general features of the environment. Long-term adaptation is called evolution and is as typical of living systems as are autosynthesis, autocatalysis, or irritability. In contrast to these characteristics, evolution is a response by a population rather than by an individual. The initial change is internal in origin and is regulated by the external environment in the form of natural selection.

The complexity of living material and the significance of evolutionary adaptation as a fundamental feature of life are demonstrated in the vast differences between the principal groups of living organisms. Evolutionary and biochemical studies indicate that all kinds of organisms, about 2,000,000 different living species, and the millions of extinct types, are descendants of a common early form of life (Figs. 1-1, 1-2, and 1-3). Each of the kinds of

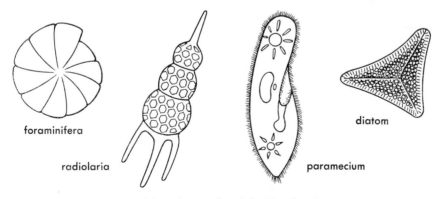

foraminifera

radiolaria

paramecium

diatom

Fig. 1-2. Typical examples of the Kingdom Protista.

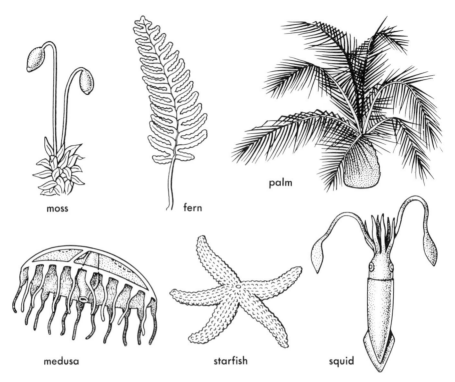

Fig. 1-3. Examples of multicellular plants and animals.

living organisms are products of adaptation to the world's many environments. Fundamentally, four major groups (kingdoms) of living creatures may
be recognized (Table 1-2). The details of the relations of the monerans and
protistans are not clearly understood, but it is evident that animals are derived from some kind of zooflagellate ancestor and that plants are closely
related to the more primitive green algae.

Although the diversity of living organisms known to exist on earth at
the present time is impressive, we must remember that a study of the earth's
history reveals thousands of kinds of extinct organisms. Fossils are the remains of dead plants and animals preserved in the record of the rocks, and
from these remnants we are able to reconstruct in broad outline the history
of living organisms. Since fossils from the oldest rocks are rather rare, the
further back in time we go the less evidence we have from fossilized remains.
On the basis of specialized dating techniques developed by astronomers,
physicists, and geologists, we believe that the earth was formed somewhere
between five and ten billion years ago. Biochemical theory indicates that life
could have first evolved from nonliving materials under the conditions probably present on the earth about three billion years ago. The first fossils are

TABLE 1-2

The Diversity of Life

PRIMITIVE FORMS

(each subgroup within the major divisions equals a phylum in formal classification)

I.   Monerans
     viruses
     bacteria
     blue-green algae

II. Protistans
     red algae   rhizopods
     cryptomonads and dinoflagellates   sponges
     yellow-green algae, golden-brown algae,   ciliates
        and diatoms   sporozoans
     brown algae   slime molds
     fungi   euglenoids
     zooflagellates   green algae

ADVANCED FORMS

III. Animals (well-organized multicellular types grouped into 20 to 25 phyla)
IV.   Plants (well-organized multicellular types, usually capable of photosynthesis, placed in two phyla)

---

known from rocks formed about one billion years in the past, thus we therefore have no record of two thirds of the history of life. Fossils and the remains of multicellular organisms become abundant in rocks of five hundred million years of age. It is obvious from these approximate dates and from Table 1-3, which shows the main course of the earth's history, that ample time for evolutionary diversification has passed since the first appearance of life on the planet earth. Perhaps equally impressive is the maintenance of the basic unity of living systems through the vicissitudes of three billion years of evolutionary change.

In summary, life is a unique, complex combination of nonliving materials expressing itself in a recognizable pattern of chemical reactivity (autosynthesis), reproduction (autocatalysis), and adaptation. The process of long-term adaptation has produced, over the three-billion-year period since the origin of living material, a diversity of living creatures, many now extinct. This diversity confirms and exemplifies evolutionary change as a fundamental characteristic of life, but at the same time it has not eliminated the essential unity of all living systems.

TABLE 1-3
The History of Life

Time (in millions of years since beginning of epoch)	Eras	Epochs	Time (as % since origin of life)	Major Evolutionary Events		Peak of Radiation	Time (on a 24-hour scale since origin of life)
				Type of Evolution	First Appearance		
1		Pleistocene	99.9	cultural	man	flowering plants insects bony fishes	11:59 PM
10		Pliocene					
30		Miocene					
40	Cenozoic	Oligocene				mammals	
60		Eocene					
75		Paleocene	96				11:00 PM
135		Cretaceous	95		mammals		
165	Mesozoic	Jurassic	94		flowering plants	reptiles	
205		Triassic	93				9:30 PM

Time	Organisms	Life	Origin	Period	Era	Age	Age
		gymnosperms		Permian	Paleozoic	92	230
	amphibians	reptiles		Pennsylvanian		91	250
			organic	Mississippian		90	280
8:30 PM	tree ferns	amphibians, insects		Devonian		89	325
8:00 PM		land plants		Silurian		88	360
		fishes		Ordovician		86	425
6:00 PM		algae; all major invertebrate phyla		Cambrian		83	500
1:00 PM		first fossils (1000)		Proterozoic	Precambrian	0	3000
12:00 midnight		first life (3000); origin of earth (10,000)	chemical; nuclear	Archeozoic		−333	10,000

HISTORICAL PERSPECTIVES

The idea of evolution, in common with most great human concepts, is not entirely of recent origin. The essence of the idea appears in Greek writings (600 BC) and probably occurred to many others throughout human history, although it was never generally accepted. Insofar as modern biology is concerned, the first clear recognition and demonstration of the fact of evolution was made by the French naturalist Jean Baptiste Lamarck (1774–1829). Lamarck's earliest paper on evolution appeared in 1801, but his principal theory was elucidated in 1815–1822. Lamarck brilliantly discerned that all life is the product of evolutionary change, that evolution resulted in the taking on of new adaptations to the environment, and that the diversity of life was the result of adaptation. Unfortunately, Lamarck developed a theory to explain how evolution occurred that does not stand up under investigation. In addition, his ideas were generally rejected by other biologists, and evolution was ignored for nearly 45 years.

Lamarck's recognition of evolution as a fact is usually overlooked by most biologists because his theory of evolution is faulty. Basically, the theory consisted of two parts: a) new structures appear because of an "inner want" of the organism; b) these structures are acquired in response to need and are then inherited by later generations. The first point is not testable by scientific methods, but the second is. In theory at least, the inheritance of acquired characteristics seems logical, particularly when we consider our legal and social system, in which things acquired by one generation are passed on to the next. In addition, all individuals do adapt their structures to the environment to a limited extent, as the skin of any habitual beach enthusiast will demonstrate. The theory is summarized in Fig. 1-4, showing Lamarck's giraffe. While the hypothesis is a valid one, it fails when subjected to scientific test. The objections to it are several: there is no known way by which somatic cells may pass characteristics to reproductive cells; experiments show no inheritance of acquired characteristics (the beach enthusiast's children are not born with a suntan); many adaptations found in organisms are not of a type that could be acquired (can an animal practice being purple?); some acquired characteristics cannot possibly be passed on (neuter sex in worker bees). Lamarck was correct in his insight as to the significance of evolution but he failed to muster a satisfactory theory to explain how it occurred.

The world was to wait almost half a century before the genius of Charles R. Darwin (1809–1882) provided the key theory of evolution and at the same time converted the scientific and intellectual worlds to acceptance of the fact of evolution. The time was ripe, the impact both within and outside of science was profound. Darwin's masterpiece was entitled *On the Origin of Species by Means of Natural Selection* and appeared November 24,

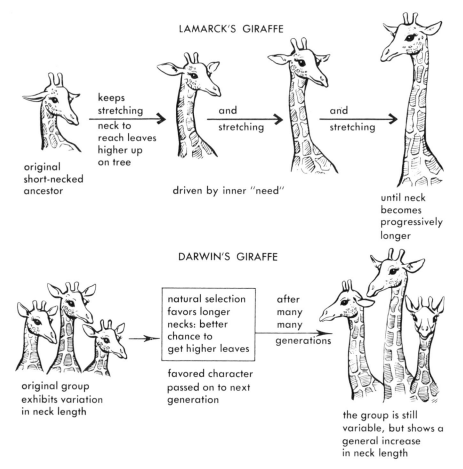

Fig. 1-4. Comparison of the ideas of Lamarck and Darwin.

1859. It became a best seller overnight and changed man's thinking forever. We cannot consider all the ramifications of Darwinism here, but interested readers are directed to the list of references. The biologically important aspects of *On the Origin of Species* include three points: the recognition of evolution as a fact; the presentation of data demonstrating the fact; and the development of a theory of how evolution took place. Darwin attributed evolutionary change to several forces, but the prime force was natural selection. His theory is based on two observations and two basic conclusions:

Facts

1. All organisms exhibit variability (look around any classroom).

2. All organisms reproduce many more offspring than survive (the North Atlantic female cod lays 85,000,000 eggs at once).

Conclusions

1. The environment selects out (natural selection) those individuals best fitted to survive, while individual variants less well-fitted fail to reproduce.

2. The characteristics thus favored by selection are passed on to the next generation.

Fig. 1-4 shows Darwin's giraffes, which evolved in a different manner from Lamarck's.

The most serious weakness of Darwin's explanation stemmed from his lack of knowledge about heredity. He was sure that differences were inherited but *how* was unknown. Darwin died before the secret of heredity was uncovered. Actually, it was discovered by a Moravian monk named J. Gregor Mendel (1822–1884) in 1865, but nobody paid any attention to his work until 1900, so that the fruits of his labor had no effect on evolutionary theory for 35 years.

Following the rediscovery of Mendel's principles a period of rapid acceleration in knowledge of heredity developed into the science of genetics. Unfortunately, early geneticists discarded almost all of Darwin's ideas because, in that egoism so typical of man, they knew something he did not know. And it even became fashionable to speak of the death of Darwinism.

During the years since 1920 it has gradually become clear that modern genetics provides the final large piece in the jig-saw puzzle of evolutionary theory. Rather than a disproving of Darwin's ideas, a cross-fertilization has occurred to produce a generally satisfactory theory of evolution based on the interaction of heredity and natural selection. It is this synthesis that forms the basis for the discussion of evolutionary processes to follow.

SUGGESTED READING LIST

CALVIN, M., "Chemical evolution and the origin of life," *American Scientist,* Vol. 44 (1956), pp. 248–263.

EISELEY, L., 1958. *Darwin's century.* Garden City: Doubleday.

IRVINE, W., 1955. *Apes, angels and victorians.* New York: McGraw-Hill.

OPARIN, A. I., 1957. *The origin of life,* 3d ed. New York: Academic Press.

WALD, G., "The origin of life," *Scientific American,* August 1954, p. 44.

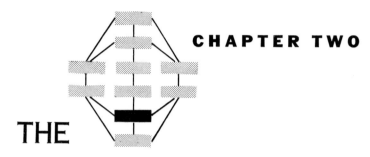

CHAPTER TWO

THE

GENETIC

BASIS OF

EVOLUTION

One of the keys to the modern theory of evolution lies in the discoveries emanating from the basic experiments carried out by Mendel and further developed by a host of geneticists during the past 60 years. These investigations provided the basic materials for unraveling the secret of biological reproduction and inheritance. Primarily responsible for our current knowledge of the mechanisms of biological heredity were Thomas Hunt Morgan (1866–1945) and his associates, first at Columbia University and later at the California Institute of Technology. A full discussion of the significant features of heredity is presented in *Genetics,* in this series, and it should be read for an expanded treatment of matters considered in this chapter. Certain other genetic ideas are surveyed here from the evolutionary viewpoint primarily to provide the reader with essential concepts basic to the thesis developed in later chapters.

One of the fundamental characteristics of living organisms is the ability to produce new individuals essentially similar to the parents. The secret of heredity unraveled by modern genetics is how reproduction takes place. A summary of our basic understanding of reproduction at present includes:

1. Development of individuals is under the control of hereditary regulators called genes; a gene appears to be composed of a deoxyribonucleic acid (DNA) and to exercise its regulatory functions by mediating the production of specific enzymes.

2. Genes in most organisms are organized into large units called *chromosomes*; chromosomes are located in the cell nucleus and may contain hundreds of genes; the number and type of chromosome are constant for

each species; some organisms, particularly bacteria and blue-green algae, lack a nucleus but hereditary material is present, dispersed in the cell; viruses correspond to one to several free-living genes.

3. The genes are capable of coordinated and exact replication of themselves and the resultant products contain exact duplicates of the hereditary regulators.

The majority of organisms are cellular and contain a nucleus and chromosomes; in subsequent discussions reference will be restricted to examples of this type.

All cells and organisms that contain chromosomes are of two general types. In most species the chromosomes occur in pairs, so that each cell contains two homologous chromosomes each with a paired series of homologous genes. This kind of cell is called *diploid* and contains 2N chromosomes. For example, all but a few cells of the body contain 23 pairs of chromosomes, the usual diploid number for man. The total number of chromosomes is 2N— that is, (2×23)—or 46. In some organisms and in all reproductive cells (*gametes*) of higher plants and animals the chromosomes are unpaired. This kind of cell is *haploid*, containing N chromosomes. In the case of diploid organisms with haploid gametes, exactly 0.5 of the chromosomes, or one from each pair, is present in the haploid cells. Again, if man is used as an example, each sperm (male gamete) or egg (female gamete) contains N, or 23, chromosomes, one from each of the 23 pairs found in the diploid cells.

REPRODUCTION

The basis of life is the reproduction of cells. In all multicellular organisms, whether they are haploid or diploid, new cells are being produced constantly by cell divisions to replace worn out or injured cells and to provide for growth. The new cells contain exactly the same number and kinds of chromosomes present in the original cells. In addition new individuals may be produced by this same type of cell division in organisms with *asexual reproduction*. In this mode of reproduction a cell divides off from the parent and becomes an independent individual. The number and kinds of chromosomes in individuals produced by asexual reproduction are exactly the same as those in the parent. The process of cell division that produces new cells or individuals with exact replicas of the chromosomal and genetic components of the parent cells is called *mitosis*. The significant features of mitosis are presented in Fig. 2-1. In the example a diploid organism is used with 2N = 4.

A second kind of specialized division in cells is characteristic of some stage of the life history of all organisms with sexual reproduction. This process is called *meiosis* (Fig. 2-2). It may occur in unicellular organisms, but in multicellular forms it takes place only in the reproductive organs, all other cellular divisions in the body being mitotic. Thus in human beings cells are produced by mitosis throughout all of the body except in the gonads (male: testis; female: ovary) where meiosis produces the reproductive cells or gametes.

The significant features of meiosis are indicated in Fig. 2-2 for an organism with a diploid number (2N) of four chromosomes. Two cell divisions occur during meiosis. In the first of these the number of chromosomes is divided exactly in half, with one chromosome of each pair going to each daughter cell. The manner of division is completely random; that is, either chromosome of a given pair may go to either daughter cell. The new cells contain 0.5 of the chromosomes from the parent and are haploid. A second division then takes place by mitosis, each haploid daughter cell dividing to produce two cells, each with a haploid number of chromosomes. The four cells produced by the second division in meiosis (the mitotic division) become the gametes. Each gamete always contains 0.5 of the number of chromosomes of the original parental diploid cell, one chromosome from each pair.

Another exceedingly important aspect of meiosis from the evolutionary viewpoint is an event that occurs during the four-strand stage (Fig. 2-3) preceding the reduction division. Frequently during the process of separation of the chromosomes as the cell divides the strands stick together and an exchange between strands takes place. The point of attachment and exchange is called a chiasma (plural, chiasmata) and is responsible for the genetic phenomenon of *crossing over*. Crossing over is an important source

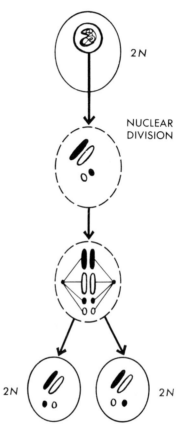

Fig. 2-1. Diagrammatic summary of mitosis.

of genetic variability and will be discussed a little later in some detail. Chiasmata formation and the results in terms of gametes are indicated in Fig. 2-3. Clearly, if one chiasma occurs between different chromosomes, two times as many gamete types may be formed as when no chiasmata are present. (How many kinds of gametes are possible when one chiasma has occurred during meiosis in an organism with 2N = 4, such as in Fig. 2-3?)

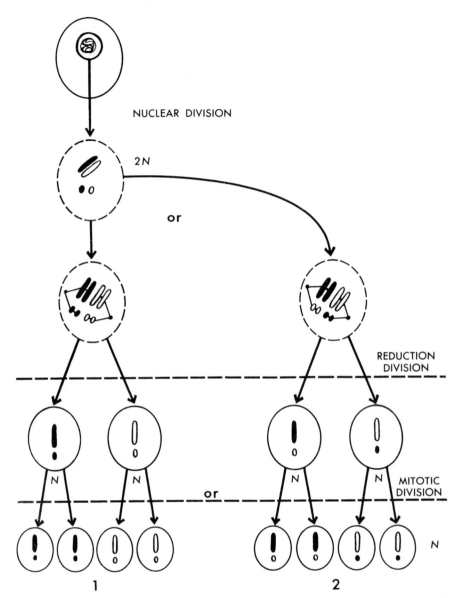

Fig. 2-2. Diagrammatic summary of meiosis.

In sexual reproduction new individuals are produced by the coming to-gether of two gametes (usually a male and a female gamete) to form a diploid cell, or *zygote*. The zygote then undergoes development into the new organism. Every sexually produced diploid organism must receive 0.5 of its chromosomal and genetic material from each gamete, or 0.5 from each parent. Meiosis is responsible for this situation and insures that exactly half of the heredity of the individual is carried by each gamete.

chiasmata may form between any two strands, at any point and several at once

PROBABILITY AND GENETICS

Because of the constant and exact manner in which chromosomes and genes are replicated in reproduction the theory of probability may be applied to the understanding of genetic and evolutionary events. In mitosis no range of possibility exists, for each daughter cell is an exact genetic duplicate of the parental cell. Probability theory is of great significance in understanding the genetics of sexual reproduction, however, since new individuals produced by this means receive in the form of discrete units exactly 0.5 of their heredity from each parent.

Most of you are familiar with probability theory as applied to the toss of a coin: what is the probability of obtaining a head on any particular toss? Or in playing cards: what is the probability of cutting the deck to a king or to the ace of spades? A better example for our discussion is to reconsider the case of meiosis developed above (Fig. 2-2). Let us for the sake of example

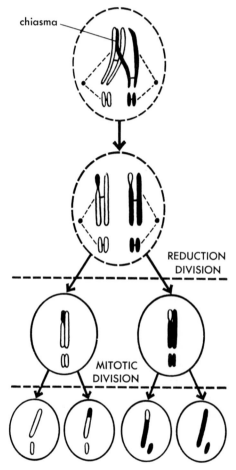

Fig. 2-3. Diagrammatic summary of chiasmata formation in meiosis.

regard the products produced by the two lineages (1 and 2) as representing the gametes of two individuals, one (1) a male, the other (2) a female. Further, we will concern ourselves only with the single pair of large chromosomes, which may be either dark or light. If it is assumed that 1000 male gametes are present, it is an obvious fact of meiosis that 500 will contain a dark chromosome and 500 will contain a light chromosome. Under these circumstances, what is the probability of sampling the gametes and obtaining one with a dark chromosome? It is clear that the chance of drawing a gamete with a light chromosome is just as likely as drawing a dark one; the events are equally probable. The next question is, how do we express these probabilities?

The general formula for the probability, P, of a single event is

$$P = \frac{f}{f+u}$$

where f is the number of ways in which the selected or favorable event may transpire and u the number of ways in which some other outcome or unfavorable events may occur. P is usually given as a fraction or decimal; $f + u$ is always equal to the total number of events. To return to the example, the number of favorable events is 500 dark chromosomes and the total number of events possible is 500 dark chromosomes plus 500 light chromosomes:

$$P = \frac{500}{1000}$$

$$P = \frac{5}{10}$$

$$P = 0.5$$

The probability of obtaining a gamete with a dark chromosome on any one draw is 0.5. (What is the probability of obtaining a gamete with a light chromosome?)

A probability of 1.0 represents certainty. The probability of drawing a gamete with two chromosomes from one of the individuals (1 or 2) indicated in the diagram is 1.0. A probability of 0 means that the event is impossible. The probability of obtaining a gamete with 7 chromosomes from the indicated individuals is 0. The probabilities for any single event ranges from 0 to 1.0. In any given situation the sum of the probabilities of all possible events *always* equals 1.0. (With these facts in mind, what is the probability of drawing a gamete containing one large dark chromosome and one small light chromosome from the mixed gametes of individuals 1 and 2 if the total number of gametes present is 1000?)

More meaningful to the problem of sexual reproduction than the probability laws relating to single events are those principles applicable to the probabilities of two or more independent events happening simultaneously. Again if we consider only the large chromosomes in the gametes (1000 male gametes and 1000 female gametes), what is the probability of a zygote being formed by the coming together of any two gametes (one male and one female)? To answer this question let us assume that fertilization has occurred at random to produce 1000 zygotes. What is the probability that a zygote will contain two light chromosomes? The probability of two or more independent events happening jointly is the product of the probability of one event times the probability of the other:

$$P = \left(\frac{f_1}{f_1 + u_1}\right) \times \left(\frac{f_2}{f_2 + u_2}\right)$$

$$P = P_1 \times P_2$$

The probability of getting in this example a male gamete with a large light chromosome is 0.5 (P_1) and the probability of getting a female gamete with a large light chromosome is 0.5 (P_2). The probability of any zygote in the sample having two large light chromosomes is:

$$P = 0.5 \times 0.5$$

$$P = 0.25$$

The probability of getting a zygote from a male gamete with a large dark chromosome and a female gamete with a large dark chromosome is similarly 0.25. Similarly, the probability of drawing a zygote with a large light and a large dark chromosome formed from a male gamete with a light and a female gamete with a dark chromosome is 0.25; the probability of the reverse situation, a zygote formed from a male gamete with a dark and a female gamete with a light chromosome, is also 0.25. In drawing zygotes from the pool of 1000 there are only these four possibilities, each with a probability of 0.25. The sum of the four probabilities equals 1.

In the example above, it is seen that while there is only one possible way in which to produce a zygote with two light or two dark chromosomes, there are two ways in which a zygote containing one light and one dark chromosome may be formed. If we are concerned only with the probability of getting a zygote of this latter type, a third probability principle is applicable. When a particular independent event may occur in more than one way its probability is the sum of the probabilities for each manner in which the event takes place:

$$P = P_1 + P_2$$

In the discussed example the probability for each of the two ways of obtaining a zygote with one light and one dark chromosome is 0.25. The probability of drawing such a zygote, without reference to the manner of origin, is:

$$P = 0.25 + 0.25$$

$$P = 0.5$$

Although the manner of determining probabilities to explain the three principles has been detailed above, it is not necessary for our purposes to work out probabilities by listing all of the possible arrangements in every case. A simple formula will serve to provide us with all of the required information. Since a zygote is always formed by the joint occurrence of two independent events (the two gametes), the expansion of the binomial $(p + q)^2$ provides the probabilities directly:

$$(p + q)^2 = p^2 + 2pq + q^2 = 1$$

p = the probability that a zygote contains a light chromosome
     $(p = 1 - q)$

q = the probability that a zygote contains a dark chromosome
     $(q = 1 - p)$

the exponent 2 indicates that two independent events involving p and q are happening simultaneously; $p + q = 1$, $(p + q)^2 = 1$.

In the expansion each term indicates the probability of a particular combination of the two events:

p^2 = the probability of a zygote with two light chromosomes
     $(p \times p)$

q^2 = the probability of a zygote with two dark chromosomes
     $(q \times q)$

$2pq$ = the probability of a zygote with one light and one dark chromosome (the 2 indicates that there are two ways to obtain this result)

This general formula may be applied to any situation involving zygote formation. For example, if the large chromosomes are ignored (Fig. 2-3), what are the probabilities of drawing zygotes produced by crossing 1 and 2 containing two small light chromosomes and two small dark chromosomes or a small light and a small dark chromosome?

The previous section of this discussion indicates the manner in which the hereditary carriers, the chromosomes, are inherited. The actual regulators of heredity, the genes, are located in a linear sequence on the chromosomes. On the paired chromosomes of a diploid cell each chromosome parallels the other in the arrangement of these regulators, and two homologous genes, one on each chromosome, are present in each diploid cell. Very frequently there are different expressions or enzyme functions of the same gene. The different expressions of a gene are called *alleles*. For example, in tomatoes the gene contributing to the control of the color of the stem has two expressions. One allele if present produces a purple stem, the other allele a green stem. The gene may be called the stem-color gene (although it does not produce stem color all by itself) and its two expressions the purple- and green-stem alleles. Each diploid tomato plant cell always contains two stem-color genes one on each of a pair of chromosomes. Obviously the tomato plant gametes always contain only one stem-color gene, since they contain only one chromosome from each pair.

In any particular individual organism any combination of alleles for a particular gene may be present. A tomato plant may have two purple-stem alleles or two green-stem alleles, or one of each. For simplification, we can symbolize these alleles as follows: p = purple stem, q = green stem. The possible combinations are: pp, qq, pq. When dealing with gene combinations the appearance of the organism is called its *phenotype*; thus the phenotype of pp is a purple stem. The actual combination of genetic materials is called a *genotype*; thus the genotype of tomatoes with a green stem is qq. In many instances, when two different alleles for a particular gene are present the phenotype appears identical to that of an individual having two identical alleles. The other allele is present and is passed on to the gametes but is masked out by what may be called the *dominant* allele. The hidden gene is called a *recessive* allele. In tomatoes individuals with the genotype pq have a purple stem (phenotype), indicating that p (purple) is a dominant allele and q (green) is recessive.

Of course, of utmost importance in considering heredity and the probabilities of gene combination is the production of gametes. Individuals of the genotypes pp and qq each produce only one kind of gamete, all p and all q respectively. Organisms producing only one kind of gamete are called *homozygous*. Organisms with a genotype of pq produce two kinds of gametes, p and q, and are called *heterozygous*. Exactly 0.5 gametes of each type are produced by meiosis.

On the basis of this information and your background in genetics (see *Genetics* in this series), solve the following problems using the expansion of the binomial.

1. Among the basic experiments carried out by Mendel was one involving garden pea plants. He crossed a homozygous for smooth-coated peas (in the pod) with another homozygous for wrinkled peas. All of the offspring had pods full of smooth-coated peas. He then allowed these individuals to breed at random. What are the probabilities for each of the following in the next generation: phenotypes for smooth and wrinkled; homozygous dominant, homozygous recessive, and heterozygous genotypes?

2. A plant breeder crossed a homozygous red-flowered primrose with a homozygous white-flowered primrose. All of the offspring were pink flowered. One of the pink-flowered individuals was crossed back to the original red-flowered plant. What are the probabilities for each of the following in the next generation: phenotypes for red, white, and pink; homozygous and heterozygous genotypes?

3. In many animals more than two alleles may be found for any particular gene. In rabbits four alleles for the coat-color gene are present. One allele when homozygous produces a dark gray coat; the second a light gray coat; the third, Himalayan coat, white with black ears, nose, feet, and tail; and finally albino. The alleles show dominance in the order given above. A Himalayan individual is crossed with an albino. What is the probability that the offspring will be albino? The same Himalayan is crossed with an individual with a dark gray coat; what is the probability that the offspring is albino?

POPULATION GENETICS

Up to this point, the emphasis has been on genes as the fundamental units of biological heredity. Genes tend to be stable elements capable of exact duplication of themselves at the time of reproduction. They are important in that no evolutionary changes are possible unless a new genetic expression (an allele) has made its appearance through faulty gene replication. Genes and biological heredity are conservative and insure the continuity of efficient adaptations. Genes, however, are not the principal units of evolutionary change.

Genes normally do not occur as discrete naked elements. With the exception of viruses, all living organisms consist of a complex mass of nongenetic material under the regulation of many interacting genes. If I may be pardoned an overgeneralization, it almost appears that all of the complexities and adaptations found in living organisms serve simply to protect, nourish, and make possible the orderly reproduction of genes. The differences between different kinds of organisms—a tiger as compared to a leopard, or a beaver compared to a redwood tree—are not due to simple differences at the gene level. Each individual is a product of the interplay of his total genetic complement, and the sum total of his genotypic adaptation to a particular ecologic niche determines his relative adaptive efficiency. Although genotypes are usually carried in the organic packages we call individuals and although individuals may be affected by evolution, individual organisms are no more primary units of evolution than are individual genes.

Research during the last 30 years, particularly by Ronald A. Fisher in Great Britain and Sewall Wright in this country, has demonstrated that evolutionary forces act not upon individual genes or individuals but upon those groups of individuals called populations. A biological population may be defined at this point as all of the individuals of the same species occurring in the same area at a particular time. Insofar as evolutionary processes are concerned, a population consists of the pooled genes of all individuals within the group, expressed indirectly through various genotypes as phenotypes. The fundamental source of evolutionary change is the impact of natural selection upon this gene pool. The population forms the stage or setting for evolution; it provides the matrix for the operation of the basic evolutionary forces; and in it individual genes may be eliminated or reproduced, individual genotypes may be eliminated or reproduced, and certain genotypic combinations may be favored over others, but the forces operate on the population pool without reference to single genes, single genotypes, or individuals. Evolution at its simplest is any change in the hereditary composition of a population.

A final genetic concept of utmost importance to an understanding of the elemental forces of evolution is the basic idea of population genetics. Each population is essentially a unit with a common body of genetic material. The fundamental discovery about the nature of these gene pools was made independently by G. H. Hardy in Great Britain and W. Weinberg in Germany in 1908. They found that the hereditary conservation of genes is a populational characteristic and that if all other factors remain constant the frequency of particular genes and genotypes will be constant in a population generation after generation. The genetic stability of populations under these conditions is spoken of as *genetic equilibrium*. Evolution only occurs when the equilibrium is upset.

An example of populational genetic analysis and the Hardy-Weinberg genetic equilibrium may be provided by study of an actual experiment. The experimenter isolated an artificial population of chickens in a large chicken coop. Two hundred chickens formed the initial population, equally divided between roosters and hens. The genetic feature studied was one of the genes regulating plumage color in these animals. On the basis of other work it is known that two alleles of one gene produce black plumage (pp) or white plumage splashed with black (qq) in the homozygous condition and that heterozygous (pq) chickens have bluish-gray plumage. One hundred chickens in the experimental population, 50 roosters and 50 hens, had black plumage, while the other 50 roosters and 50 hens had splashed-white plumage. The chickens were allowed to breed at random so that every possible genotype would be produced. The questions a populational geneticist would ask are: What are the frequencies of a particular allele in the population? What will be the frequencies of the genotypes and phenotypes in the next generation? These are simply questions of probability: What is the probability that any gamete will contain a particular allele? What is the probability that any zygote will contain any particular combination of two alleles?

In the experiment described above, the original population consisted of chickens homozygous for black plumage (pp) or splashed white (qq). Chickens with black plumage produce only one kind of gamete, whether sperms or eggs, with a genetic constitution of p. Splashed-white chickens similarly produce only gametes with a genetic constitution of q. Within the population of 200 individuals there is a gene pool of 400 plumage-color genes (200 black alleles and 200 splashed-white alleles) since each diploid individual contains two genes for plumage color. The gene frequency of p is thus equal to 200/400 or 0.5, and the gene frequency of q is also equal to 200/400 or 0.5. One half of the total gametes produced by the studied population are of each type.

From this information it is possible to predict the genotypic and phenotypic frequencies in the next generation, a prediction verified by the results of the random crosses. With only two kinds of alleles there are only three ways in which the gametes may combine at random to form new chickens. Some p gametes will combine with p gametes. Other p gametes will combine with q gametes. Finally, some q gametes will combine with other q gametes.

The probabilities of any two gametes coming together to form a zygote is the product of their frequencies. It is obvious that the same relationships apply here as in the examples in the previous section on probability and can be developed by an expansion of binomial: $(p + q)^2 = p^2 + 2pq + q^2 = 1$. In this case $p = .5$ and $q = .5$. Substituting in the formula gives us the probabilities for each genotype:

$$(0.5 + 0.5)^2 = 0.25 + 0.5 + 0.25 = 1$$

$$\begin{matrix} pp & pq & qq \\ \text{black} & \text{blue} & \text{splashed white} \end{matrix}$$

The significance of genetic equilibrium is demonstrated if we carry our experiment on for one more generation. In the first generation we had two genotypes and in the second generation three genotypes. What will be the situation if the population of second-generation individuals are allowed to breed at random with one another? We do not need to know the absolute number of individuals since we already know that they are in the proportion of 25 percent black, 50 percent blue, and 25 percent splashed white. What will be the genotype frequencies in the next generation? What are the gene frequencies of the second parental generation? Let us begin by determining the gene frequency of the allele p in the second parental population. We know that for every 100 individuals in the population there are 200 genes. Twenty-five out of 100 individuals are of the genotype pp; that is, they contribute 50 p genes to the total pool of 200. In addition, 50 out of 100 individuals have the genotype pq, and thus contribute 50 p genes to the pool of 200. No other individuals have p genes. Thus we see that 100 genes out of the total of 200 are p. The frequency of p is 100/200 or 0.5. If p is 0.5, then q must also be 0.5, for ($q = 1 - p$). The gene frequencies for p and q both equal 0.5, just as they did in the previous generation. What will be the frequencies of the three possible genotypes in the next (third) generation? $p^2 = 0.25$, $2pq = 0.50$, $q^2 = 0.25$. These values added together equal 1.0. Is there something familiar here? Of course, for since the gene frequencies are the same, the genotype ratios are also the same in the new generation. In fact, unless there are changes in conditions, the gene frequencies and genotype frequencies will remain constant throughout all subsequent generations. This example may be extended into a fundamental rule. Once a population reaches genetic equilibrium ($p^2 + 2pq + q^2 = 1$), the genetic frequencies will always be the same generation after generation, unless the equilibrium is upset.

Gene frequencies are rarely exactly equal in natural populations. A geneticist analyzed a group of tomato plants growing on an abandoned field as "escapes." He found that in 1000 plants selected at random, 510 had purple stems and 490 had green stems. What are the frequencies of the two alleles for stem color? What percentage of the population is heterozygous for the stem-color gene?

Or, as another example, a farmer started with a flock of 100 chickens of which 90 were splashed white and 10 were black. He allowed free interbreeding for many years. What are the gene frequencies and genotype frequencies in this flock after 65 generations?

It is now apparent to biologists that the fundamental units of evolution are populations of genetically similar individuals more or less isolated spatially from other similar populations of the same species. The pooled genes of the population tend to form a stable unchanging equilibrium of genotypes that remains constant from generation to generation. Genetic equilibrium is an expression of the conservative nature of biological heredity, which favors the genetic *status quo* through exact replication of the genes in cell division. Evolution can never take place unless this equilibrium is upset. The mode of evolution at the populational level is partially determined by the characteristics of the population and the relative frequencies of the raw materials of variation, the genes. The equilibrium may be upset if conditions change either within the population through origin of additional variability or through external environmental changes. The elemental forces of evolution, mutation, natural selection, and genetic drift are radical elements that counter genetic equilibrium and bring about evolutionary change. If equilibrium is maintained, evolution is impossible. If the equilibrum is modified by any factor or factors, evolution has occurred.

SUGGESTED READING LIST

Horowitz, N. H., "The gene," *Scientific American,* October 1956, p. 78.

Mazia, D., "How cells divide," *Scientific American,* September 1961, pp. 101–120.

Peters, J. A. (ed.), 1959. *Classic papers in genetics.* Englewood Cliffs, N.J.: Prentice-Hall.

Sutton, H. E., 1961. *Genes, enzymes and inherited diseases.* New York: Holt, Rinehart and Winston.

PART II

THE FUNDAMENTAL EVOLUTIONARY PROCESS

CHAPTER THREE

THE

ELEMENTAL

FORCES

OF EVOLUTION
Two fundamental patterns of evolution appear to be responsible for the changes that have produced the incredibly complicated labyrinth of diversity comprising the world of life. Evidence from the fossil record makes it clear that these two patterns have been repeated over and over during the history of life, while modern genetics provides a basis for the understanding of the forces producing the observed patterns. These patterns include diverse changes across the entire spectrum of organic diversity, from the evolution of characteristics of penicillin-resistant populations of the bacterium *Staphylococcus* to the magnificent radiations of the reptiles and flowering plants. The driving evolutionary forces at the base of the changes remain the same but under different circumstances different results are obtained.

BASIC PATTERNS OF EVOLUTION

Evolution at its simplest involves relatively minor changes in the gene pool of a particular population from one generation to the next, with corresponding modification in genotypic frequencies and the range of phenotypic variation. No new populations result from the change but the descendent population is not genetically identical with its predecessor. Evolution of modified gene pools from pre-existing ones is called *sequential evolution*. Paleontologists working with short-time series, geneticists studying laboratory populations, and field biologists investigating isolated natural populations repeatedly verify the reality of sequential evolution within the history of a single population.

An example of sequential evolutionary change is provided by a combined genetic and field study of the scarlet tiger moth (*Panaxia dominula*). During a period of 14 years (1939 through 1952) a group of British geneticists studied the fluctuations of gene frequencies in a single population of this form. The species is ideally suited for such study since none of the adults of the previous generation survives the winter. Fig. 3-1 indicates the fluctuations of gene frequencies for one pair of alleles in this population. In one expression of the gene the black anterior wing of the moth has numerous light spots; the second allele produces a wing with two light spots. In heterozygous individuals there are several light spots in the wing. The fluctuations in gene frequency are given for normal and two-spot alleles. Note the significant changes between some generations (1940 and 1941) and the slight changes between others (1947 and 1948). No sign of genetic equilibrium exists here. Indeed, once we realize that in every population thousands of genes are present and subject to change, it becomes apparent that equilibrium is exceptional and sequential evolution the rule. All available evidence indicates that almost all populations undergo change of this sequential type every generation.

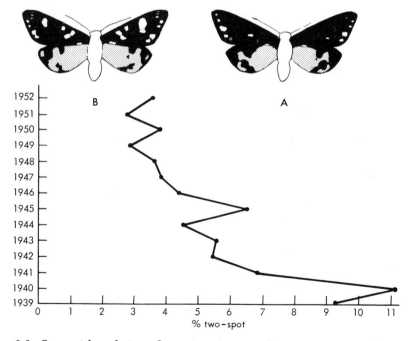

Fig. 3-1. Sequential evolution: fluctuations in gene frequency in a population of scarlet tiger moths during a 14-year period.

Sequential evolution may produce rather random fluctuations over long periods of time with relatively little difference between the genotypic combinations and frequencies at the beginning and end of the studied period. It may also result in gradual shifts in gene combinations so that the descendent population is markedly different from its original ancestor. Sequential evolution, by itself, never produces new populations from old, but only produces temporal changes in a population continuum. In one sense, sequential evolution reflects the conservative nature of biological inheritance.

The second major pattern of evolution usually is the result of forces operating over a longer period of time than those responsible for sequential changes. The second pattern is one of *divergent evolution*, that is, the origin of new populations or organisms from old ones. Divergent evolution is most familiar to scientists working with the fossil record, but the diversity of the organic world at the present time is the result of divergence after divergence to the hundredth power over the course of three billion years. Paleontologists

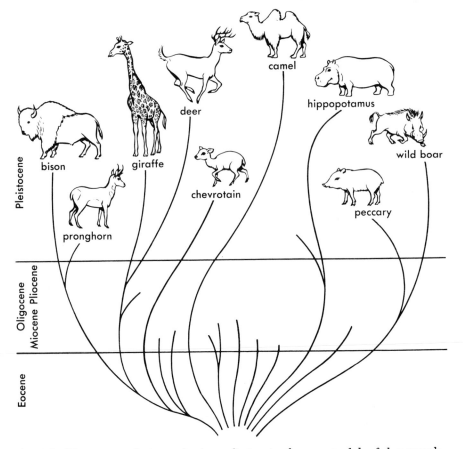

Fig. 3-2. Divergent evolution: adaptive radiation in the even-toed hoofed mammals.

see divergent evolution documented in the rocks where new populations develop as fragments of old populations and divergence compounded on divergence radiates over the millions of years of records in a vast if not overwhelming array of organic diversity. Divergent evolution is responsible for the myriad modifications superimposed upon the basic framework of living material to produce the spectrum of organisms from tuberculosis bacterium to towering redwood and humble flea. An exciting example of evolutionary divergence is provided by the radiation of the even-toed hoofed mammals, illustrated in Fig. 3-2. The basic ancestor of this line was also ancestral to the odd-toed hoofed mammals and the carnivores.

The difference between sequential and divergent evolution as described in the above paragraph perhaps overemphasizes the differences between them. Sequential evolution is not known to be exclusively characteristic of any population, since all populations seem to fragment or undergo divergent evolution if they are studied over a long enough period of time. Sequential evolution continues in the diverging new populations. However, while the elemental evolutionary forces responsible for sequential change also contribute to a great degree to divergent evolution, additional factors must cooperate to produce the latter. The two processes are intimately related but they are not identical. Sequential evolution and divergent evolution are graphically compared in Fig. 3-3 to emphasize the obvious differences within the qualifications mentioned above.

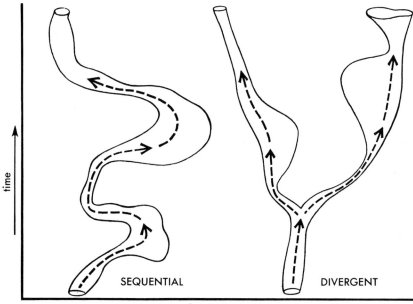

SEQUENTIAL   DIVERGENT

range of variation in genotypes

Fig. 3-3. Comparison of sequential and divergent evolution.

In recognition of the two basic patterns of evolution, sequential and divergent, the remainder of this book is divided into two sections for discussion of the two sets of processes. The first section treats with the elemental forces of evolution common to both processes and the manner in which these forces combine to bring about sequential change. The final section of the book deals with the way in which the elemental forces are modified by the impact of additional factors leading to evolutionary divergence.

The reality of the differences between sequential and divergent change must not be overlooked in discussing evolution. It is only a few years since many workers thought that divergence could not possibly be explained in terms of the elemental evolutionary forces and many others failed to see that divergent evolution involves more factors than those responsible for sequential change. Even today the relationship between the two processes, while clear in most aspects, remains the subject of some controversy. The argument developed in Chapters 8 and 9 is designed to clarify and interrelate the distinctive features of both patterns of evolution.

THE ELEMENTAL FORCES AND MICROEVOLUTION

The processes of sequential and divergent evolution are driven by the same elemental evolutionary forces, although additional factors contribute to divergence. These forces guide the course of populational evolution, are in control of all sequential change, and provide the basic impetus for evolution in divergent new populations. We have already seen that the mechanism of biological heredity operates to produce genetic equilibrium. If all factors remain constant the gene frequencies never fluctuate from generation to generation but maintain this equilibrium. In addition we have seen that equilibrium in naturally occurring populations is rare, if it ever occurs at all. In the case of the scarlet tiger moth (Fig. 3-1), for example, evolutionary change took place in each generation, at times only slightly modifying the gene pool, at others markedly modifying it. What are the forces responsible for these sequential changes? How do they operate to produce evolution?

Evolution at its simplest involves changes in the frequencies of a single pair of alleles from one generation to the next. The factors that produce these frequency changes are the elemental forces. If we refer to the example of the scarlet tiger moth (Fig. 3-1) the effect of these forces may be briefly considered. The forces of evolution are responsible for the shifting pattern of gene frequencies throughout the 14 years. Any one of three primary forces of evolution could have produced the recorded changes seen between the frequencies of each succeeding generation.

1. *Mutation and variation.* A change in gene frequency may be produced by an increase in any of the alleles present or by the appearance of new alleles, through spontaneous change (mutation). Mutation as an evolutionary force is the ultimate source of new alleles and new gene combinations

(variation). Variation provides the hereditary materials to be molded by the impact of the other two forces. In most instances other factors contribute to the effect of variation by modifying and amplifying the effect of spontaneous gene mutation.

2. *Natural selection.* The sum total of environmental factors may operate to favor the differential reproduction of certain alleles or gene combinations over others present in the population. The impact of the total environment on the reproduction of gene combinations is the force of natural selection. The effects of natural selection change as the environment changes, so that slightly different conditions each generation favor slightly different gene combinations. Natural selection molds the genetic variation present in a population, but it cannot directly produce new genes or gene combinations.

3. *Genetic drift.* In many small populations completely random fluctuations of alleles or gene combinations may occur by chance, even under constant environmental conditions. These fluctuations constitute genetic drift, which must also make its impact felt through random effects upon the genetic variation already present in the population.

Variation through mutation of two-spot (p) to normal (q) alleles might have been the mechanism that was responsible for producing the change between 1940 and 1941 generations of the scarlet tiger moth. A slight change in the environment may have enhanced the survival and reproduction of more normal alleles between the two generations, or in other words, natural selection favored the normal over the two-spot allele. Finally, the shift might be due to random effects in this small population or genetic drift from two-spot to normal alleles. Unfortunately, we do not know exactly which force or forces produced the observed changes. Actually, all three forces probably are involved to some degree over the 14-year period, with the change between generations at any point being the result of interaction between all three forces rather than the effect of a single force.

Evolution resulting from interaction of variation, natural selection, and genetic drift to produce relatively small population changes is frequently called *microevolution.* Sequential evolution is always the product of the microevolutionary process; divergent evolution at its simplest is also microevolutionary. The rest of the present section of this book deals with the process of sequential evolution through microevolution. The contributions of the elemental forces of variation, selection, and drift will be treated in detail with a discussion of their interactions in this basic process.

SUGGESTED READING LIST

CARTER, G. S., 1951. *Animal evolution.* London: Sidgwick and Jackson.
FORD, E. B., 1955. *Moths.* London: Collins.
SMITH, J. M., 1958. *The theory of evolution.* Harmondsworth: Penguin.

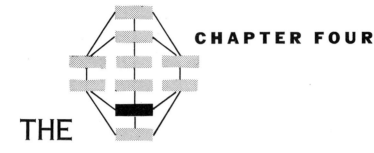

CHAPTER FOUR

THE

SOURCES OF

VARIATION
"No two individuals are exactly alike" and "All organisms exhibit variation" are biological clichés expressing the most obvious feature of living organisms. We need go no farther than any classroom to appreciate the reality of variation. Look around a class at the characteristics of the human individuals in the sample. Almost any feature selected for analysis will demonstrate the point; hair color, eye color, skin pigmentation, or singing voice—each exhibits a spectrum of variation. No two individuals are precisely alike, because they are a combination of various variants of a great many attributes. Two individuals may agree in having blue eyes but differ from one another in almost every other respect. The overwhelming number of possible combinations of characteristics produces biological individuality.

Differences between individuals within the same species may be the result of either hereditary or environmental effects. The latter are of no importance to evolution since they are not inherited by the next generation. The offspring of a man who has lost a finger in an accident are not born lacking the same finger. Hereditary differences under the control of the genetic makeup of the individual are the raw materials of evolutionary change. This type of variation and the patterns it produces are the essential media of evolution. The variation exhibited by human beings in eye color, hair color, skin pigmentation, and singing voice are all under the control of genes within the human population pool. The combinations of these genes with thousands of others result in the formation of distinctly individual human beings. But where did the genetic variation come from in the first place? Why are there blue eyes, green eyes, gray eyes, brown eyes, and black eyes? What are the sources of hereditary variation?

These are among the most trenchant of evolutionary questions, since we know that evolution cannot take place without variation in hereditary characteristics. Darwin recognized the central position of hereditary variation as a force in evolutionary change, but it is only with the discoveries of modern genetics that an explanation of heredity and the sources of inherited variation have been elucidated. Without a knowledge of these features our current concept of evolution would remain at an unsophisticated level.

Thanks to the brilliant work of geneticists from a wide variety of fields and eras, biologists now recognize four primary sources of genetic variability:

A. Mutation
  1. gene
  2. chromosomal

B. Recombination
  3. heterozygosis (cross between two kinds of homozygous parents)
  4. crossovers (genetic exchange between chromosomes)

Mutations are regarded as being the source of new and different genetic material appearing in a population. Recombination is responsible for spreading the mutants through the population and developing new combinations of new genetic materials with older genotypes. Special features of mutation and recombination and considerable detail on their characteristics are presented in *Genetics*, in this series. The discussion that follows emphasizes points of significance to evolution.

GENE MUTATION

In the early days of genetic study the small fruit fly, *Drosophila melanogaster,* was selected as an excellent laboratory animal for hereditary experiments. In one of the laboratory colonies of normal red-eyed fruit flies there appeared in 1909 a single white-eyed male. No white-eyed fruit flies had ever been reported until the appearance of this odd individual. When this male bred with red-eyed females in the laboratory it was discovered that the white eye is due to an allele recessive to the red-eye allele. This spontaneous appearance of a new gene expression is called a *gene mutation*. The mutant individual is always descended from normal parents of a pure-breeding line and his peculiarity is passed on to the next generation. Since the appearance of the white-eye allele about 5000 spontaneous mutant individuals have been found among nearly 20,000,000 fruit flies examined in the course of genetic studies. A great many different genes are known to have undergone spontaneous changes, from those controlling wing size to those affecting bristle length or eye structure. Some mutations have occurred several times, others only once, but each has increased the genetic variability of *Drosophila*.

Gene mutations are now known for every kind of plant or animal that has been subject to genetic study—including corn, snapdragons, coffee, cacao, mice, molds, bacteria, and men—and they seem to be a universal fact of life. Many of the differences between individuals of the same population are ultimately the result of gene mutation and the subsequent establishment of genetic equilibrium between the original allele and the mutant. The other principal features of gene mutation are summarized as follows:

1. Genes are very stable. About one gene mutates for every 20 gametes produced in *Drosophila*; since each gamete contains about 20,000 genes, this is a low rate of change; actually the figure is probably higher since many slight mutations pass unnoticed.

2. Each gene has a characteristic mutation rate; mutation rates for a number of genes in corn (*Zea*) are summarized in Table 4-1.

TABLE 4-1

Mutation in Corn (Zea)

Genes	Mutation rate per 1,000,000 gametes
seed color	492
seed-color inhibitor	106
purple seed color	11
sugary seed	2.4
yellow seed	2.2
shrunken seed	1.2
waxy seed	0

3. Gene mutation is a change in genetic material, not a loss. Many genes are known to mutate from a mutant allele back to the original expression (reverse mutation); in *Drosophila* the forked-bristle (q) allele is a known mutant of normal bristle (p); however, occasionally the reverse mutation from forked bristle to normal bristle occurs: ($p \xrightleftharpoons{\text{mutates}} q$).

4. More than one kind of mutation is possible for any particular gene. Some genes mutate to several different alleles, the basis for the presence of several alleles for one gene (multiple alleles).

5. Most of the obvious mutations are deleterious to the organism but most mutations are neither obvious nor deleterious. The significance of the first portion of this statement is more apparent than real and indicates the emphasis on abnormalities and striking mutations as a method of genetic analysis; in *Drosophila* approximately 500 genes are known through discovery of mutations; since the chromosomes of this animal are estimated to contain 20,000 genes and since we now realize that many mutations involve subtle chemical and physiological changes not expressed as major visible modifications, it seems likely that the majority of mutations are not deleterious at all.

6. Rates of mutation may be modified experimentally. A number of agents including x-rays, cosmic rays, ultraviolet rays, gamma rays, temperature, and a variety of chemicals produce changes in mutation rates for all genes in exposed chromosomes. The type of mutation caused by such agents has no relation to the nature of the stimulus; rather, the mutants will be of the same types found in other populations of the same organism.

7. Mutation appears to be the result of a slight change in the chemical structure of the groups of specialized DNA molecules that are the genes; differences in the DNA structure are apparently translated into production of different enzyme systems, and the new or mutant DNA is capable of replication to be inherited by succeeding generations.

Succinctly stated, a gene mutation is any change in the chemical organization of the gene that is replicated and passed on to succeeding generations. It must be emphasized that mutation is random in the sense that the environmental stimuli that activate the chemical change act randomly, and the mutations they produce have no direct relation to the stimulus. A rise in temperature will increase mutation rates in *Drosophila*, but mutations occur in a great many genes and not necessarily in any that control temperature tolerance or adaptation in the fruit fly. At the same time, mutation is nonrandom, since under a given set of circumstances mutation rates and mutant genes appear generation after generation in a constant pattern. We also know that certain genes mutate to certain alleles under the regulation of other genes. Mutation, although at one time thought to be rare, occurs as slight and nonobvious changes at a significant rate. Many aspects of the mutational process still need investigation and in them lie opportunities for future elucidation of genetic and evolutionary problems.

Gene mutations are the ultimate source of hereditary variation. By themselves their impact upon populational variability may be slight. Gene mutants, however, usually have amplifications of great significance because of their interactions with other genes besides their homologous alleles. The indirect effect of these interactions is frequently of greater significance in the development of a variety of genotypes and phenotypes and their impact on the course of evolution than is the direct effect of the mutant allele.

The simplest examples of gene interactions and their contributions to variation are provided by analysis of phenotypic results of the interactions of two genes (each with two alleles). A diagram of plumage inheritance in parakeets (Fig. 4-1) shows the significance of interaction in increasing the number of phenotypes. The interactions of the two sets of genes (p_1, q_1) (p_2, q_2) produce four plumage colors depending upon the gene combinations present. The combination p_1p_2 will be green. The combinations $q_1q_1p_2p_2$ and $q_1q_1p_2q_2$ will be yellow. The combination $p_1p_1q_2q_2$ will be blue, but so will $p_1p_1p_2q_2$; $q_1q_1q_2q_2$ will be white. This type of interaction is called *epistasis* and is very common.

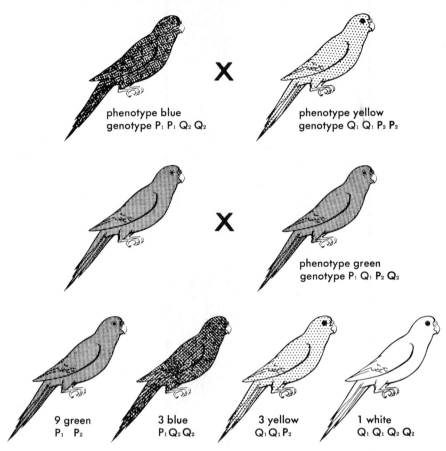

phenotype blue
genotype $P_1 P_1 Q_2 Q_2$

X

phenotype yellow
genotype $Q_1 Q_1 P_2 P_2$

X

phenotype green
genotype $P_1 Q_1 P_2 Q_2$

9 green
$P_1 \quad P_2$

3 blue
$P_1 Q_2 Q_2$

3 yellow
$Q_1 Q_1 P_2$

1 white
$Q_1 Q_1 Q_2 Q_2$

Fig. 4-1. Plumage inheritance in parakeets under control of two independent genes.

More complex than epistasis but based upon the same pattern of gene interaction are characteristics regulated by several different genes, each contributing only a small effect to the total phenotype. These groups of genes are called *polygenes*. An example of polygenes is provided by the factors regulating skin pigmentation in man. The actual number of genes controlling pigmentation is thought to be four (possibly more), with at least two alleles for each gene. The range of possible genotypes is 136, each with a slightly different degree of pigmentation in phenotypic expression.

Another source of variation is provided by multiple alleles. The regulators of human blood types are an example. Only a single gene is involved but it occurs as three distinct alleles, p, q, and r. In addition, while both p and q are dominant to r, neither is dominant to the other. The possible phenotypes and genotypes for human blood types are summarized in Table 4-2. In the case of some genes as many as 11 alleles are known with 66 genotypes.

TABLE 4-2

Human Blood Types

Group	Genotype
AB	*pq*
B	*qq* or *qr*
A	*pp* or *pr*
O	*rr*

Another feature of the genes that contributes to variation is the phenomenon of *pleiotropism*. Many genes are now known to affect more than one characteristic, and such genes are called pleiotropic. The allele that produces vestigial wings in *Drosophila* also causes a modification in the balance organs, certain bristles, and sperm and egg production, among other characters. It seems likely that all genes have multiple effects, just as it is probable that many genes are involved in the development of any characteristic of an organism.

A final indication of the interdependence of genes lies in the discovery that the location of the gene in relation to other genes determines interactions and characters. In some of the chromosomal mutations discussed below, gene positions are changed and new characteristics appear although no gene mutation has taken place. The new characteristics are due to interactions between genes that are now positioned in a new relationship to one another.

All of these comments on gene activity emphasize one important conclusion. An individual is the result of interactions involving his total genotype, and every gene plays a part in the process. A mutation that by itself is of little significance may contribute mightily to variation through its effect on gene action and interaction.

CHROMOSOME MUTATION

Chromosome mutations differ only in degree from gene mutations. If the chromosomes undergo spontaneous reorganization or modification the effect is usually more pronounced than if only a single gene mutates. Chromosomal mutations are inherited once they occur and are of a considerable variety:

A. Changes in number of chromosome
   1. loss or gain of part of chromosomal set: nondisjunction
   2. loss of an entire set of chromosomes: haploidy
   3. addition of one or more sets of chromosomes: polyploidy

B. Structural changes in chromosomes
1. changes in number of genes
    a. loss: deletion
    b. addition: duplication
2. changes in gene arrangement
    a. exchange of parts between chromosomes of different pairs: trans-location
    b. rotation of a group of genes 180° within one chromosome: inversion

Any of these major changes contributes to variability by changing the pattern of gene interaction with particular emphasis on magnification of the role of position effect. Although chromosomal mutations are now well known and are sometimes striking in their phenotypic effects, for all practical purposes they may be treated in the same way as gene mutations in discussing microevolution.

RECOMBINATION

In view of the nature of gene action and the great significance of cooperation between the genes, the process of mixing or recombining the available genes into a variety of genotypes rivals mutation as the primary source of variation. The full import of recombination as a source of genetic variation and as an equal partner with mutation in the manufacture of the materials of evolution is clearly recognized by biologists. Recombination— that is, new genotypes from already existing genes (old wine in new bottles) —is of two kinds: 1) the production of gene combinations containing in the same individual two different alleles of the same gene (half sherry and half port), or the production of heterozygous individuals; 2) the mixing of a particular allele with a series of genes not previously associated with it, by an exchange between chromosomal pairs during meiosis, called crossing over, to produce new gene combinations. The significance of both recombination processes may be shown by comparing the possibility for variation in an asexually and a sexually reproducing population.

If we assume two populations each homozygous in every gene, but one reproducing asexually and the other sexually, the importance of recombination and also of sex will be seen. First let us consider heterozygosity. A single mutant ($p \rightarrow q$) for one gene occurs in each population. In the asexual population all the offspring of the single individual in which the mutation occurred will be heterozygous (pq), while all other members of the group will remain homozygous (pp) as will their offspring. Without hetero-zygosity, no variation would be present. In the sexual group three genotypes will develop, since once the new allele is established it will combine at random in gametes. The genotypes are *pp*, *pq*, *qq*. In other words, from one gene mutation the latter population is a full 33 percent more variable. Multiply this instance by 10 genes or 100 genes and the amount of potential variation produced by heterozygosity in a sexual population becomes fantastic, far outstripping the impact of the mutant alleles.

If we continue along this line it will be immediately apparent that crossing over during meiosis does not occur in asexual reproduction and the second contribution of recombination can only operate in sexually-reproducing organisms. Mutation and restricted heterozygosity are the sole sources of variation for asexual reproducers. Crossing over is an added dividend from a variational and evolutionary viewpoint to the process of sexual reproduction. Sex is not essential for the reproduction of new individuals; it is a luxury. It is a luxury, however, that insures greater potential for evolution and flexibility of adaptation than is ever possible for asexual forms.

Crossing over is produced during the process of meiosis by chiasmata (Fig. 2-3). The process produces an exchange of genetic material between homologous chromosomes. In a more detailed example (Fig. 4-2), imagine a population in which all individuals are of the following genotypes: *no*, *pq*, and *rs* for three genes on the same chromosomes. If no crossing over ever occurred, all gametes would be *npr* or *oqs*. However, since chiasmata are formed at almost every meiosis, new gametes and gene combinations are produced and four kinds of gametes appear, *npr* and *oqs*, plus two new ones, *nqr* and *ops*. Crossover thus speeds the mixing of new mutant alleles with the genes already present. In this example the impact of crossing over increases the number of possible genotypes from three to ten. If all possible crossovers occurred, six new gametes could appear (the two already mentioned and *nqs*, *opr*, *nps*, and *oqr*). A more complicated but also more realistic example is found in the contribution of crossovers to human variation. As you will recall, there are 23 pairs of chromosomes in human beings, each with several thousand genes. Chiasmata may form at any point on these chromosomes, and a moment's thought will provide an appreciation of the utterly overwhelming potential for new gene combinations, and in turn for new kinds of individuals, provided by crossover. Since each point of chiasmata formation doubles the number of kinds of gametes, the gamut of human variation visible around us is no longer surprising but merely attests to the efficacy of recombination.

The significance of recombination to evolution cannot be overestimated. A single mutational change may be lost or passed on without great impact on a population, but if its effect is modified and enhanced by recombination an unending contribution to variation is begun. Variation is the raw material for evolutionary change; recombination is its principal source. Mutation alone has relatively little effect on variation without the pervasive impact of recombination.

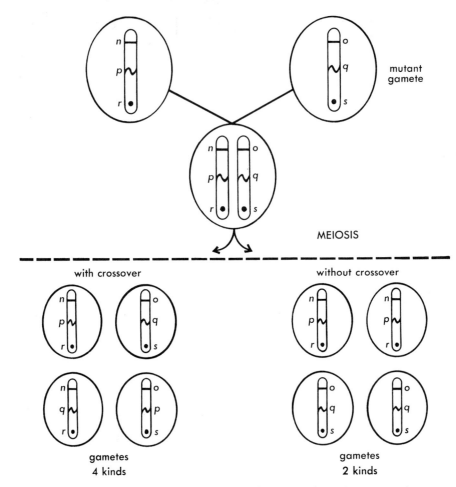

Fig. 4-2. Diagrammatic illustration of the relative number of gene combinations possible as a result of recombination.

VARIATION AND EVOLUTION

The simplest possible change in the genetics of a homozygous population, all individuals of which have exactly the same genotype, would be the production of a single mutant allele $p \rightarrow q$. If the mutation constituted a slight change of a not too deleterious kind, or even if it were wildly advantageous, its effect on the population would be small. In fact, if the mutation occurred only once, the next generation would be at equilibrium and no change would subsequently occur unless conditions changed. Imagine, for example, that the original population contained only 50 individuals (100

p genes). After one p mutates to q the gene frequencies are $p = 0.99$, $q = 0.01$; the genotypes of the next generation, $pp = 0.9801$, $pq = 0.0198$; $qq = 0.0001$. Forever afterward, if conditions remain constant, the equilibrium remains the same, again illustrating the unimportance of a single mutation.

As already indicated, however, in most instances gene and chromosomal mutations occur at a regular rate each generation.

In corn, the mutation rate (μ) for a number of alleles has already been indicated (Table 4-1). If a population initially homozygous for the seed-color gene is studied, it is obvious that the gene frequencies of the population will change from one generation to the next as follows:

$$\Delta p = -\mu p$$

Δp is the rate of change in gene frequency and μ is the mutation rate $p \rightarrow q$. In the first generation the change may be computed

$$\Delta p = - (0.492 \times 10^{-4}) \ 1.0$$
$$\Delta p = - 0.0000492$$

The new gene frequencies will be

$$p = 1.0 - 0.0000492 = 0.9999508$$
$$q = 0.0000492$$

If the mutation rate is unopposed, equilibrium will be reached when the population becomes homozygous for q. If the frequency for p in any generation is represented by p_o, the frequency for p any number of generations (n) later is:

$$P_n = P_o \ (1 - \mu)^n$$

Mutation in this simple case clearly is a driving force for slight evolutionary change through the impact of continuous mutation rates. In actuality, reverse mutation $(q \leftarrow p)$ and the other evolutionary forces counteract and modify the drive toward complete change produced by mutation and contribute toward the maintenance of variation. Evolution may consist of nothing more than a change of gene frequencies from one generation to the next as a result of mutation pressure, but it is rarely so simple. A number of genes are undergoing regular mutational changes, recombination is mixing the genes into new gene combinations, and all of the factors contributing to variation are under the impact of other evolutionary forces. The origin of variation through mutation is a central feature of evolution, but by itself it produces no long-lasting or profound changes. The other forces cannot operate without variation, but their impact far outranks mutation as the guide for evolutionary change.

Evolution is based upon variation and changing gene frequencies. Variation itself does not constitute evolutionary change, but is a prerequisite for evolution. The force of mutation responsible for the origin of hereditary variation may directly modify gene frequency and produce evolutionary change. Recombination acts to enhance the effects of mutation by assembling a broad spectrum of gene combinations. It modifies and intensifies the contribution of mutation, but it cannot be regarded as an evolutionary force since it never changes gene frequencies. Recombination looms large in the evolutionary process because it provides the bulk of genetic variability that is worked upon by the forces of selection and drift to produce major evolutionary change. Mutation and recombination provide the source of variation and an effective agent for its spread through the population. Together they develop the genetic materials for evolution.

SUGGESTED READING LIST

DOBZHANSKY, T., 1951. *Genetics and the origin of species.* New York: Columbia University Press.

LEVINE, R. P., 1962. *Genetics.* New York: Holt, Rinehart and Winston. In this series.

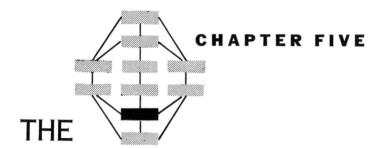

CHAPTER FIVE

THE

ROLE

OF NATURAL

SELECTION

The idea of natural selection as the guiding force of evolution was the principal contribution of Charles Darwin to evolutionary theory. Darwin's original concept of selection was rather unsophisticated and negative and was applicable to individuals rather than populations, but his recognition of this essential principle provided the key to understanding evolutionary processes. Darwin saw the process of evolution as a struggle for existence between individual organisms. Since all species produce many more offspring than survive, he concluded that the total environment eliminated those individuals least fitted for survival and encouraged the survival of the fittest. The environment thus acted as a selective force, sorting out those variants best adapted to the particular environmental circumstances. The impact of the environment on hereditary characteristics was natural selection and led to descent with modification. Natural selection favored the features of an organism that brought it into a more efficient adaptive relationship with its environment, and accounted for the fact that every living creature is constructed to live in a certain environment.

The theory of natural selection has had a twisted history since Darwin's day. Complex selection was believed to be the only source of evolutionary change by many nineteenth-century biologists, while it was completely repudiated by others. Among those who rejected selection as a force in evolution were the early twentieth-century geneticists confident in their new-found knowledge of heredity and certain that since Darwin hadn't known Mendel's principles, he couldn't have known very much about anything else either. It is ironic that selection today forms the only scientifically tenable solution

to the problem of evolutionary change and that its reinstatement in a modified form is principally the result of data accumulated by the intensive and
brilliant studies of populational geneticists.

THE NATURE OF NATURAL SELECTION

In our discussion of evolutionary forces up to this point we have
considered the mechanism of inheritance and the genetic sources of variation.
We have noted that under standard environmental conditions all genes in a
populational gene pool come to equilibrium and that the equilibrium is
maintained. Evolution does not take place under such circumstances because
evolution means change, not equilibrium.

The key to understanding evolution thus lies not in knowing the source
of variation but in finding out how the balance between various gene combinations is modified so that the composition of the population changes. One
way in which small evolutionary changes may occur is through mutation, but
unidirectional mutation always results ultimately in a new homozygous equilibrium. The single force primarily responsible for upsetting genetic equilibrium is natural selection.

Natural selection at its simplest is the impact of any factor in the total
environment of an organism tending to produce systematic genetic change
from one generation to the next. Or stated another way, it is any environmental feature producing a relative change in the reproduction of certain
genes. Natural selection brings about evolutionary change by favoring differential reproduction of genes. Differential reproduction of genes produces
changes in gene frequency from one generation to the next. Natural selection does not produce genetic change, but once change has occurred it acts
to encourage some genes over others.

Selection is further characterized by its invariable encouragement of
genes that assure the highest level of adaptive efficiency between the population and its environment. When two or more gene combinations are present,
selection favors increased reproduction of the gene combination most efficient
under the environment circumstances. Evolution through selection brings
about improvement in adaptive relations between organisms and their environment. Selection has been the principal force operating over millions of
years to facilitate the development of new adaptations to the world's environments and is responsible for the evolution of the present diversity of life.
The interaction of mutation, recombination, and selection results in new
adaptive relations between organisms and their environments and forms the
process of adaptation.

An experimental example of selection as a force in genetic change is
provided again by the white-eyed mutant *Drosophila*. If white-eyed males

are the only mates available, white-eyed and wild-eyed (normal) females will breed with them. But if the total environment is changed by including both white-eyed and wild-eyed males, the manner in which selection operates is seen (Fig. 5-1). The original experimental population is composed of 50 percent wild-eyes and 50 percent white-eyes. Obviously, unless environmental conditions are important the population will remain at equilibrium forever. In actuality, however, both white- and wild-eyed females seem to be reluctant, if not revolted, at the prospect of mating with white-eyed males, and because of the differential mate selectivity the white-eye gene quickly is eliminated from the population. Female mating preference thus is one factor in the total environment of this population. It acts as one selective force producing a regular systematic change in gene frequencies. It also produces an adaptive improvement, since wild-eyed males have a better environmental relation (they reproduce) than white-eyed males.

Natural selection is a creative force in evolution since it favors and encourages efficient gene combinations. Unfortunately, Darwin emphasized the negative aspects of selection and created the notion that it is a ruthless force, eliminating some individuals while favoring others. The idea of Darwinian selection was based upon differential mortalities that may result in differential reproduction, but this type of selection is only one part of the total force of selection. No white-eyed males were killed in the example given

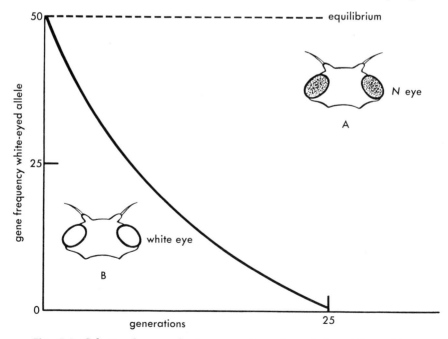

Fig. 5-1. Selection for eye color in an experimental population of *Drosophila*.

above, yet selection effectively eliminated the nonadaptive white-eye allele. Or perhaps it is better to say that it encouraged the wild-type allele to take over the population. In any event, selection creates new adaptive relations between population and environment, by favoring some gene combinations, rejecting others, and constantly molding and modifying the gene pool. Innumerable laboratory studies support the active, positive role of selection in the modification and evolution of populations.

THE INTERACTION OF VARIATION AND SELECTION

Because the environment is never stable but undergoes almost constant, if frequently minor, change, the nature of selection also fluctuates. It seems probable that many of the slight changes in gene frequencies known to occur in natural populations between generations are due to changing selection pressures (Fig. 3-1). Nevertheless, on rather long-term bases the forces of selection tend to channel variation along particular lines of environmental stability. From the viewpoint of populational genetics the influence of long-term selection may be measured as it affects the differential reproduction of genes.

If selection in a theoretical population of organisms is considered, several significant points will emerge. Suppose that the population when first studied contains two alleles for a particular gene (p and q). One allele (p) is dominant over the other (q). The gene frequencies are $p = 0.9$, $q = 0.1$. The population will contain three genotypes, pp, pq, qq. If the population were at equilibrium the gene frequencies will remain constant, but suppose that investigation reveals a differential reproduction due to selection, favoring the dominant allele. The effect of selection is represented by the selection coefficient s, which indicates the force of natural selection operating against the recessive allele. Assume that the value of s is 0.1, in this example. Since the two genotypes pp and pq are not affected by selection, in this case they produce equal numbers of offspring. However, the genotype qq produces fewer offspring relative to the numbers produced by pp and pq. The relative proportions of offspring produced by the several genotypes are measured by an adaptive value (W). If selection operates in the manner discussed above, the adaptive values are $pp = 1$, $pq = 1$, and $qq = 1 - s$, or 0.90. From these data the impact of selection from one generation to the next may be calculated (Table 5-1).

If the same selection pressure continued indefinitely, ultimately the recessive allele would be eliminated and equilibrium established. The differences between genes in adaptive value may be illustrated by another summary (Table 5-2). In all cases in this table selection favors p over q. The initial frequencies are standardized: $p = 0.5$, $q = 0.5$. Different amounts of selection produce different results in gene reproduction, but selection—no matter how small—will ultimately establish the favored gene.

In most cases in nature, selection rarely operates without conflict with mutation. If mutation is taking place from $p \rightarrow q$, the following formula gives the change in gene frequency:

$$\Delta q = \mu p - sq^2(p)$$

The value μp measures the rate of mutation adding q to the population; the value sq^2, the loss through selection. Using this formula, solve the following problem, given these values: originally $p = 0.6$, $q = 0.4$; $\mu = 0.00001$; $s = 0.001$. Calculate the gene frequencies for the next generation.

TABLE 5-1

Changes in Gene Frequency Produced by Selection

	Genotypes			
	PP	Pq	qq	Totals
W	1	1	$1 - s$	$\overline{W}$
Initial gene frequencies	$p^2 = .81$	$2pq = .18$	$q^2 = .01$	1
Frequency after selection	p^2 (0.81)	$2pq$ (0.18)	$(1-s)q^2$ (0.009)	$1 - sq^2$ 0.999

Frequency of p in next generation $= p/1 - sq^2 = 0.901$; frequency of $q = 0.099$.

TABLE 5-2

Changes in Gene Frequency Produced by Different Amounts of Selection

s	1.0	0.6	0.1	0.01	−0.5
W	0	0.4	0.9	0.99	1.5
Initial gene frequency (p)	0.5	0.5	0.5	0.5	0.5
Frequencies after selection (p)	0.67	0.58	0.5128	0.5012	0.444
Increment of gene frequency of p	+0.17	+0.08	+0.0128	+0.0012	−0.056

NATURAL SELECTION IN ACTION

The force of selection as a prime evolutionary force was seen clearly by Darwin in the natural world. He cites innumerable examples of adaptation through selection, and thousands of new cases are recognized each year. But one problem in discussing selection has usually been the correlation of experimental laboratory studies under controlled conditions with what actually happens in nature. During the last twenty years a series of combined experimental field studies have been carried out on the problem of industrial melanism in moths, and they provide an exciting insight into the operation of selection under natural conditions. These brilliant investigations were undertaken originally by R. A. Fisher and E. B. Ford and more recently by H. B. D. Kettlewell, all of Britain.

The original study was based upon the peppered moth (*Biston betularia*) (Fig. 5-2). These moths were well known to amateur collectors of the nineteenth century. Up until 1845 all known specimens were light in color, but in that year a single black moth of this species was taken at the growing industrial center of Manchester. Presumably at that time its highest frequency in the population was not more than 1 percent. As time passed, more and more black peppered moths were taken, until by 1895 the black form comprised 99 percent of the Manchester population. Today only a few light-

Fig. 5-2. Left: Dark and light forms of the peppered moth on the trunk of an oak at Birmingham, England. Right: Dark and light forms of the peppered moth on an oak in an unpolluted area. (Courtesy of H. B. D. Kettlewell.)

colored populations persist and most areas support populations homozygous for the black phenotype. This change in gene and genotype frequencies corresponds beautifully with the spread of industry in England during the past 120 years. The change from light to dark color in the sooty, dirty, coal-dust-covered areas of England seems an excellent example of natural selection favoring an inconspicuous color pattern matching the darkened vegetation. Since the initial studies on the peppered moth about 70 other species in Great Britain have been found to exhibit similar adaptive trends. The phenomenon, now called industrial melanism, is also known for European industrial areas, and about 100 species of moths in the Pittsburgh region of the United States exhibit a similar evolutionary change, with black forms, originally rare, taking over in conjunction with the march of industry.

Observation of the changes in gene frequency did not provide unquestioned proof of the role of natural selection in establishing industrial melanism in moths. Of course, the fact that the vast majority of forms exhibiting industrial melanism are species that rest on the surfaces of vegetation, the exact places where soot is thickest, further confirmed the theory of selection. Almost all evolutionists accepted the changes in the peppered moth and other forms as a marvelous example of protective coloration being taken on as an adaptive advance at a rapid rate, but confirmation was still lacking. Final proof was provided by Professor Kettlewell's ingenious experiments on the significance of color in protecting the moths from their only predators, birds. He released known numbers of marked individuals of the peppered moth into two areas 1) a bird reserve in Birmingham, an industrial area, where the local population consisted of 90 percent black moths; 2) an unpolluted Dorset countryside where no black moths occurred. He released 477 black and 137 light individuals at the Birmingham site. From a distance he was able to watch birds feeding on the released moths, and he recovered the surviving moths by attracting them to a light at night. The recaptures consisted of 40 percent of the black moths and 19 percent of the light moths. At the unpolluted locality 473 black moths and 496 light moths were released. The results of the recaptures were just the reverse of those at Birmingham. Only 6 percent of the black moths were retaken, but 12.5 percent of the whites. Obviously natural selection in terms of bird predators plays an enormously significant part in industrial melanism.

A further significant experiment verifies the role of natural selection in this case. Both at Birmingham and Dorset birds were filmed in the act of taking the moths from locations where equal numbers of both black and light individuals were on tree trunks. At the former site 15 black and 43 light moths were eaten; at the latter, 164 black and 26 light. The rapidity of change from light to dark color variants in areas of industry within natural populations of moths attests to the efficacy of natural selection as a creative evolutionary force.

SUGGESTED READING LIST

DARWIN, C. R., 1859. *The origin of species by means of natural selection.* (Numerous editions.)

FISHER, R. A., 1929. *The genetical theory of natural selection.* New York: Dover.

MULLER, H. J., "The Darwinian and modern conceptions of natural selection," *Proceedings of the American Philosophical Society,* Vol. 93 (1949), pp. 459–470.

SHEPARD, P. M., 1959. *Natural selection and heredity.* New York: Harper & Row.

STEBBINS, G. L., JR., "Reality and efficacy of selection in plants," *Proceedings of the American Philosophical Society,* Vol. 93 (1949), pp. 501–513.

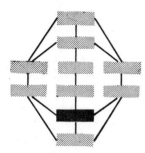

CHAPTER SIX

GENETIC

DRIFT The force of natural selection acts upon variation to encourage favorable gene combinations and to eliminate unfavorable ones. The result is always the same, the development of more efficient adaptive relationships between a population and its environment. The significance of selection in evolution and its impact on populations of organisms is so overwhelming that many evolutionists were led to believe that *all* microevolutionary changes are attributable to the interaction of variation and selection. Concomitant with this belief was the concept that *all* evolutionary changes are adaptive in nature. Selection interacting with variation does account for a great deal of evolutionary change but recent studies indicate that selection is not the only force acting on variation to produce change.

Evidence from naturally occurring populations clearly indicates that variational differences between populations of certain species cannot have been stabilized by selection. Numerous cases of nonadaptive variation between populations are known to field biologists, and these cases pose a puzzling difficulty when selection is considered the only driving force in evolution. In some populations, genetically controlled characteristics appear to be of neutral selective value, yet they persist. Other characters are nonadaptive but are fixed in certain populations. Typical examples are discussed in Chapter 8.

The occurrence of nonadaptive or neutral gene combinations produced in spite of selective pressure has also been demonstrated experimentally in laboratory populations. Studies in populational genetics principally by Sewall Wright have led to the recognition of a third elementary evolutionary force responsible for the fixing in populations of nonadaptive or neutral characteristics. This force, genetic drift, or Sewall Wright effect, plays an important role in populational evolution.

FIXATION OF NONADAPTIVE OR NEUTRAL CHARACTERS

Genetic drift as a force in microevolution interacts with variation to produce changes from one generation to the next. Drift, however, operates significantly only in very small populations. It has no importance in microevolution of large or moderate-sized population units.

The basis for the effect of drift is a matter of probabilities. Imagine a small homogeneous population of just two individuals. A single mutation of $p \rightarrow q$ produces a single heterozygous individual. The heterozygous individual crosses only with the homozygous member of the population, hence only offspring of pp or pq are produced. If an extremely large number of offspring are born they will usually be in equal ratios of pp and pq. But because of the laws of probability, the ratios of genotypes will be various if the numbers of offspring are 0, 1, 2, 3, 4, 5 . . . n. If no offspring are produced or none live to maturity the mutant is lost. If one offspring survives, the probability that the mutant survives is 0.5; if two survive, 0.25, etc. However, all of the offspring, whether 1 or 10, may contain none of the mutant allele or they may all contain the mutant. If only one offspring is produced it may be pq (0.5) or pp (0.5). If 10 are produced a number of combinations occur:

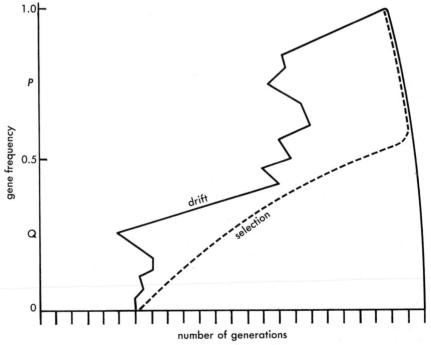

Fig. 6-1. Differences between effects of genetic drift and selection on gene frequencies.

10 *pp*; 9 *pp* and 1 *pq*; 8 *pp* and 2 *pq*; 7 *pp* and 3 *pq*; 6 *pp* and 4 *pq*; 5 *pp* and 5 *pq*; 4 *pp* and 6 *pq*; 3 *pp* and 7 *pq*; 2 *pp* and 8 *pq*; or 1 *pp* and 9 *pq*. If any situation other than 5 *pp* and 5 *pq* results, one genotype and one allele will be unbalanced in the genetic pool. In succeeding generations the random process continues and within a short time the mutant is eliminated or all individuals become homogeneous for it.

This principle applies to all small populations. The various probabilities for 0:10, 1:9, 2:8, 3:7, 4:6, 5:5, 6:4, 7:3, 8:2, 9:1, and 10:0 are different but each may occur. The results are at random and are responsible for random genetic fixation or loss of the mutant gene. Loss or fixation occurs regardless of selection pressure, hence the name genetic drift.

This genetic luck of the draw and resultant chance loss or fixation of the mutant does not occur in large populations for obvious reasons. If the original population consisted of 1000 individuals and one mutation occurred, there would be 1999 *p* genes and 1 *q*. Without strong selection pressure favoring *q*, it will have little probability of gaining control of the population, although it may persist if it is not overly deleterious. In large populations drift cannot operate against selection. The different influences of drift and selection on populations are compared (Fig. 6-1) to emphasize this point.

The essential feature of drift is that the smaller the population, the greater are the random variations in gene frequencies. In a small population the random effects of drift cause the mutation to be lost or fixed; the entire population becomes homozygous within a few generations. Drift is fickle; it may reproduce one allele in abundance one generation and the other the next, but loss or fixation of one allele or the other is inevitable. Since most species of organisms consist of partially isolated small populations, the role of genetic drift in microevolution is considerable.

SUGGESTED READING LIST

WRIGHT, S., "Evolution in Mendelian populations," *Genetics*, Vol. 16 (1931), pp. 97–159.

———, "On the role of directed and random changes in gene frequency in the genetics of populations," *Evolution*, Vol. 2, (1948), pp. 279–294.

CHAPTER SEVEN

THE

RESULT

OF EVOLUTION:

ADAPTATION
The end product of evolutionary change is establishment of organisms that function more efficiently in a certain environmental situation than did any predecessors. At the populational level the taking on of better adaptive relations to a changing environment is accomplished primarily through the interaction of mutation and selection, but other factors may enhance the effect of these forces, and genetic drift may be antiadaptive. In evolution above the population level another complex of forces contributes to the development of more efficient relationships between organisms and their environments.

Any characteristic that is advantageous to a particular organism or population is called an adaptation. The lungs of land vertebrates make possible gaseous exchange between these organisms and the air and are an adaptation for terrestrial life. The reality of adaptation is confirmed by the diversity of life and the thousands of environmental situations inhabited by life. The millions of different adaptations found among living organisms—from the photosynthetic pigments of plants, the webs of spiders, and the roots of trees to the complex locomotor devices of fish, bats, and horses—provide us with the fact of evolutionary change. The great contribution of Jean Baptiste Lamarck to evolutionary thought was his careful demonstration of the universality of adaptation in living organisms and his recognition of adaptation as the result of evolutionary change.

The acquisition of adaptive features through the interaction of evolutionary forces is the process of adaptation. Lamarck's attempt to explain the process of adaptation was incorrect and for this reason his contributions to evolutionary thought are usually overlooked. His demonstration of the fact of evolution and the reality of adaptation was finally vindicated by Darwin, who developed a more cogent explanation of the process of adaptation.

ADAPTATION AND ENVIRONMENT

Most books about evolution devote a considerable amount of space to presenting evidence for evolution. Invariably the evidence consists of the enumeration of adaptations, usually different adaptive functions of the same structure or fossil histories of structural development. The universal existence of adaptation need not be belabored here. The fact that organisms are alive and reproduce offspring of the same kind is in itself proof of adaptation. Any organism, including the reader of this book, is marvelously adapted for existence on earth, and each species exhibits an impressive series of general and special adaptations for life in a particular environment. General adaptations are usually most important in the long-term evolution of a major group of organisms, while special adaptations are developed for restricted and specialized adaptive relations to a small segment of the available environment.

The sand lizard (*Uma scoparia*) of the Mojave Desert of California (Fig. 8-1) exhibits both general and special adaptations for life on desert sand dunes. The special adaptations, which include fringed toes, shovel nose, valvular nostrils, modified eyelids, color pattern, and the behavior of swimming under the surface of the sand, are advantageous for dune life. Less obvious, but perhaps even more significant to life on wind-blown dunes, are the general adaptations of the camera eyes, lungs, circulatory system, digestive tract, nervous system, and many other features found in all lizards and most terrestrial vertebrates.

Adaptation as a process has produced living forms in tune with the requirements of their total environment. The complexity of the total environment explains the complexity of adaptation and the necessary compromises between adaptations to conflicting environmental forces. All living organisms live in an environment comprised of the physical and biotic influences of their particular ecosystem and are adapted in an extremely complex way to the matrix of interacting factors:

A. Physical environment: physical and chemical factors
B. Biotic environment
    1. extraspecific environment: biotic community
    2. interspecific environment: population
    3. internal environment: individual

THE PROCESS OF ADAPTATION

The several forces responsible for evolutionary change—mutation, selection, and drift—have each been considered as more or less independent elements in preceding chapters. In actuality, all three forces probably operate contemporaneously in most populations. The basic process of microevolution consists of changes in gene frequencies in a population from one generation to the next as guided by the elemental forces. The forces upset the genetic equilibrium to produce microevolutionary change.

The elementary process of evolutionary adaptation involves microevolutionary change brought about by the interaction of variation and selection (Fig. 7-1). Selection operates on the available variation to produce a gene pool more efficient in its interaction with the particular environment than that of the preceding population. Any change in variation through mutation or recombination provides new grist for the evolutionary mill as the grindstone of natural selection sorts out some gene combinations and favors others. A complicating factor in this simple pattern is genetic drift, which may also affect variation but does not usually favor adaptation.

As we have discussed the elemental forces, emphasis has been placed on single genes for the sake of explanation. In all known cases of microevolu-

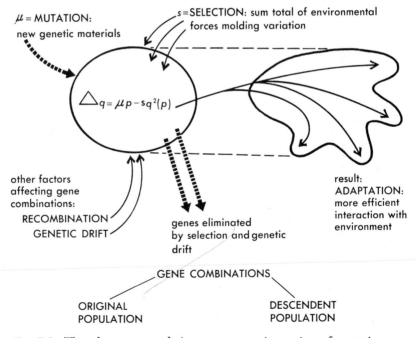

Fig. 7-1. The elementary evolutionary process: interaction of mutation, recombination, selection, and drift to produce adaptation.

tion, however, many genes and gene combinations are under the influence of hundreds of environmental factors. Changes in gene frequency are rarely as simple as our examples imply. Evolution even at its simplest is an extremely complicated process. Selection molds the spectrum of variation into new patterns of adaptation in a continuously changing environment, resulting in change in the environment-organism relations.

Microevolution through the interplay of the three elemental forces of evolution probably produces changes in all populations from one generation to the next. Microevolution also is responsible for the differences that arise between related populations. Additional evolutionary forces usually cooperate with mutation, selection, and drift to produce new populations from pre-existing ones, and the process of adaptation is usually involved (Fig. 7-1). The fragmentation and development of new populations is called *speciation* and will be considered in detail in Chapter 9.

At another level, fragmentation involves the origin and evolution within a short time of a great many adaptive types. This pattern of fragmentation may involve a number of species populations but usually occurs above the species level. It is called *macroevolution, or adaptive radiation.* While microevolution and speciation tend to produce special adaptation, macroevolution usually develops from a general adaptation with a number of special adaptations following from the general one. Macroevolution is characterized by 1) subdivision of the group into many new subgroups; 2) an invasion of numerous new environmental situations; and 3) diversification of structure and biology.

Finally, on rare occasions, new combinations of characteristics cause the appearance of new biological organizations of general adaptation. The evolution of these new and rare organizational adaptations forms *megaevolution.* Macroevolution and megaevolution are discussed more fully in Chapter 10.

TABLE 7-1

Levels of Evolutionary Change

Process	Basic pattern	Result
microevolution	sequential	adaptive, neutral, and nonadaptive changes in gene combinations
speciation	divergent	adaptive changes in isolated related populations
macroevolution	divergent	adaptive diversification and radiation
megaevolution	divergent	origin of major new adaptive biological organizations

All the levels of evolution differ from one another to a considerable degree in fundamental features but all are based upon the microevolutionary process and all contribute to adaptation. Microevolution alone produces sequential adaptive change, while speciation, macroevolution, and megaevolution produce divergent adaptation. At all levels, the result of evolution is the same: the development of organisms adapted to a changing environment and having a more efficient relation with the present environment than any predecessors. With the singular exception of microevolutionary genetic drift, the forces and processes of evolution lead to higher and higher levels of adaptation between organism and environment (Table 7-1).

SUGGESTED READING LIST

COTT, H. B., 1940. *Adaptive coloration in animals.* London: Methuen.
DOBZHANSKY, T., 1955. *Evolution, genetics and man.* New York: Wiley.
DODSON, E. O., 1960. *Evolution: process and product.* New York: Reinhold.
GRANT, V., 1953. "Pollination." *Encyclopedia Americana.*
MARSHALL, N. B., 1954. *Aspects of deep sea biology.* London: Hutchinson's.

PART III

EVOLUTIONARY
DIVERGENCE

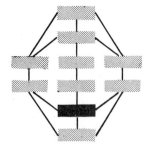

CHAPTER EIGHT

RACES,

SPECIES,

AND

ISOLATING

MECHANISMS
Anyone who has some familiarity with the living world realizes that organisms are not uniformly distributed over the earth's surface. Even if we study a single species—for example the sand lizard, *Uma scoparia* of the Mojave Desert in California, which has a rather restricted habitat of wind-blown sand dunes—it soon becomes apparent that the individuals are not evenly distributed over the species range. Further investigation will demonstrate that even on a single sand dune the individual lizards are not evenly dispersed but tend to occur in irregular clusters (Fig. 8-1). Detailed study reveals that each of these small groups of individuals acts as a distinct unit. The sand lizards within the unit interact with one another, select their mates from adjacent individuals in the group, and rarely wander across the intervening gap to associate with lizards from other similar groups. Additional investigation indicates that members of each group resemble one another very closely in genetic features and differ slightly from the other groups on the same dune. Each of these clusters of individuals forms a population partially isolated both spatially and genetically from other similar populations.

These groups of genetically similar individuals bearing an intimate temporal and spatial relation to one another form the smallest population units, called *demes*. Each deme is isolated to some extent from adjacent demes but there is always the possibility of genetic exchange between them.

Even distantly located demes may contribute genetic material to one another over a period of time by the gradual passage of certain genotypes from one deme to another. Demes are open genetic systems that are affected by gene flow from adjacent populations; that is, they are only partially isolated populations.

The largest populational unit is called a *species*. This kind of population is usually made up of several to many demes, and although each deme is partially isolated from other demes within the species population, there is always some potential for genetic exchanges. Species populations, however, unlike the individual demes of the same species, are closed genetic systems, protected against gene flow from other species through complexes of genetically regulated isolating mechanisms.

In the basic pattern of sequential evolution, there is almost constant change in genetic constitution within a population from generation to generation. The interaction of variation, selection, and drift functioning within the limits of the population structure are responsible for these continuing and

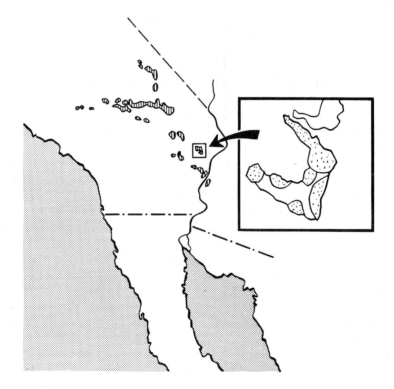

Fig. 8-1. Distribution of Mojave sand lizard, *Uma scoparia*. The map indicates the basic geographic distribution of the species, and the insert the distribution of individuals and demes on a single sand dune.

gradual changes. It is almost as though the three evolutionary forces were struggling for control of the population. In one generation variation may gain the upper hand as the effects of selection and drift are reduced by population size or a changing environment. Selection may be most efficacious in the next generation, eliminating to a considerable degree the gains made by variation. Drift, of course, usually operates to the detriment of both selection and variation. At any one time the genetic composition of the population is a compromise between the effects of the three warring forces. Over a period of time a population may undergo enough change to become distinct from the original ancestral deme. However, the kind of evolution producing changes between generations of the same population does not in itself explain the origin of new populations.

In the remaining chapters we will analyze the manner in which the elemental forces of evolution produce new populations from the old. The forces involved are fundamentally the same as those operating in sequential evolution, reinforced by additional factors to bring about evolutionary divergence. The major feature of organic evolution is the production of new adaptive types through a process of populational fragmentation and genetic divergence.

VARIATION IN BIOLOGICAL POPULATIONS

That evolutionary divergence is a fact seems amply illustrated by the diversity of living organisms. The manner in which diversity arises, however, is only understandable if we appreciate the patterns of variation found in biological populations. We know that evolution takes place at the population level, and an understanding of variation at this level provides a basis for understanding how evolutionary divergence comes about.

We have already mentioned the general nature of the largest populational unit, the species. At this point it is appropriate to present a more formal definition as a basis for discussion of intraspecific variability. We know that a species is a population usually made up of a number of genetically similar demes that replace one another spatially or ecologically. The demes within the species are only partially isolated from the other demes and may exchange genetic materials with one another when temporally in contact, as when an individual from one deme wanders into the area of another deme during the breeding season. In addition we know that all of the demes of a particular species are genetically isolated from demes making up other species. A species may be characterized as follows: a natural population in which the individuals are actually or potentially capable of breeding with one another and do not normally or successfully interbreed with individuals of other such populations, under natural conditions.

We recognize two patterns of genetic isolation between related species. In some cases two very similar populations may be widely separated from one another by a geographic or ecologic barrier. For example, the southern elephant seal, *Mirounga leonina*, occurs in the cool waters of the Southern Hemisphere around Antarctica, the southern coasts of South America, South Africa, Australia, New Zealand, and many of the antiboreal islands. A close ally, the northern elephant seal, *Mirounga angustirostris*, is found in cool waters along the coast of western North America. The two forms are very similar to one another and can be distinguished only with difficulty. However, the breeding populations of the two forms are separated by about 3000 miles of warm tropical seas, and hence are not capable of genetic exchange. Where forms occupy discrete geographic or ecologic ranges separated from one another by spatial barriers they are called *allopatric populations*. The two kinds of elephant seals are allopatric species genetically isolated by an ecogeographic barrier.

The second pattern of genetic isolation occurs in cases where related populations share a portion of their ecologic ranges. Such populations are called *sympatric* and they are isolated from one another not by space but through the physiologic expression of genetic difference. The salamanders of the genus *Taricha* exemplify this situation. *Taricha torosa*, the California newt, is found from southern California northward into north-central California. The Pacific newt, *Taricha granulosa*, occurs from southern Alaska south along the Pacific coast to the San Francisco Bay region. The two populations are sympatric in central California both to the north and to the south of San Francisco. Even though these newts may breed at the same time and in the same streams, no genetic exchange takes place between them because of differences in breeding behavior, egg deposition, and developmental patterns. Allopatric populations may be isolated from one another by physiological differences as well as distance, but the essential significance of genetic isolating mechanisms is expressed only in sympatric species.

Within species populations there are a number of characteristic variation patterns. These patterns are the result of the activity of the elemental forces of evolution, and description of the patterns forms a basis for the analysis of the origin of evolutionary divergence. For our purposes the following variational patterns will be considered:

A. Random variation
B. Nonrandom variation (ecologic variation)
   1. races
   2. clines

Among many species of plants and animals variation appears to form a random pattern. In these cases each deme within the species population differs slightly from adjacent demes. When the distribution of the entire species is viewed the variation presents a chaotic pattern having no discernible correlation with differences in the environment in the various areas within the species range. A typical example of random demic variation is provided by the ocellated klipfish, *Gibbonsia elegans*, a common fish along the coast of western North America. Each deme in this species exhibits its own combination of peculiarities apparently unaffected by the characteristics of immediately adjacent demes. One character, body depth, shows a fascinating spectrum of variability, from a population with an average body depth of 16.9 percent of the body length to one with an average body depth of 20.4 percent of the body length. If these two demes were considered alone, the individuals could always be recognized as coming from one deme or the other on the basis of body depth. Other demes are intermediate between these two extremes, and although they are all partially isolated from one another some genetic exchange occurs. Significantly, the body-depth character exhibits a random pattern of ecogeographic distribution within the species. In this variation pattern the genetic differences between the several demes do not seem to be correlated with habitat differences.

In many other organisms variation is nonrandom and tends to be closely correlated with differences in the ecologic conditions in different portions of the species range. In many cases the species appears to be composed of groups of essentially similar demes that inhabit large portions of the total range. The demes within the several segments usually share a large number of basic characteristics. When the segments appear to be different in genetic makeup and are readily recognized they are called *races* or *subspecies*. Demes found in the areas intermediate to the ranges of particular subspecies usually exhibit characteristics of both adjacent forms. These intermediate populations form a zone of intergradation or genetic flow between the races. The western rattlesnake, *Crotalus viridis* (Fig. 8-2), is an excellent example of ecologic fragmentation. Nine geographic races are recognized and each race occupies a distinctive ecologic area within the total range of the species. The races differ in characteristics of body proportions, scutellation (arrangement of scales), and coloration. Intergrading populations are found whenever any two races of this rattlesnake come into ecologic contact.

Frequently the ecologic forces responsible for divergence operate at a local level to produce a great many slightly different races. The western pocket gopher, *Thomomys bottae*, is a particularly plastic form capable of adaptation to a wide spectrum of conditions in soil, food supply, vegetational cover, temperature, and humidity. In consequence a large number of ecologic races are readily recognizable within the species, based upon pelage (body coat) difference, size, and skeletal proportions (Fig. 8-3). Each population within the species is adapted for existence in a very small ecologic segment of the total range. Each forms a distinctive partially isolated ecologic race.

Another interesting aspect of the general phenomenon of racial variation is the tendency for certain rather similar adaptive types to develop inde-

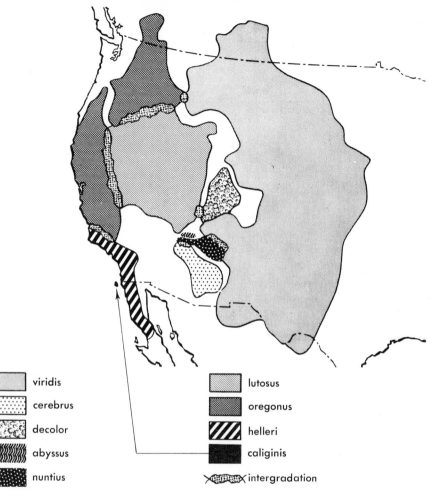

viridis		lutosus	
cerebrus		oregonus	
decolor		helleri	
abyssus		caliginis	
nuntius		intergradation	

Fig. 8-2. Geographic variation in the western rattlesnake, *Crotalus viridis*.

pendently throughout the geography of the species. In the case of the pocket gophers, populations living on the same general soil types resemble one another very closely in color of pelage, even though their ranges may be hundreds of miles apart. These populations occur under similar ecologic conditions and their similarity suggests that the basic features held in common represent adaptations for the same kinds of environmental circumstances.

An additional example of the parallelism of ecologic adaptation is provided by the hawkweed, *Hieracium umbellatum*, of Sweden. In this plant, populations occur in four principal habitats: shifting coastal sand dunes, sandy fields, sea cliffs, and woodlands. Throughout the entire species range, demes established on coastal sand dunes resemble one another in basic adap-

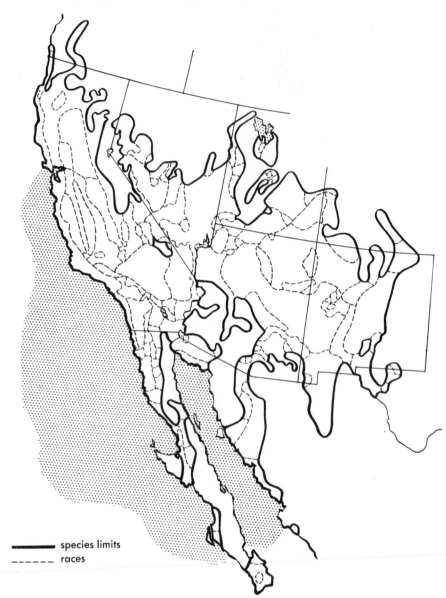

—— species limits
– – – – – races

Fig. 8-3. Ecologic fragmentation of races in the western pocket gopher, *Thomomys bottae*. Numerous local races have developed in this species in response to local ecologic conditions.

tive features. Other adaptations are shared by all sandy field populations, others by those living on sea cliffs, and still others by woodland populations. The sand dune populations are separated from one another by populations of the woodland type (Fig. 8-4) but have apparently responded to similar selective influences. In characteristics not of particular significance to sand dune

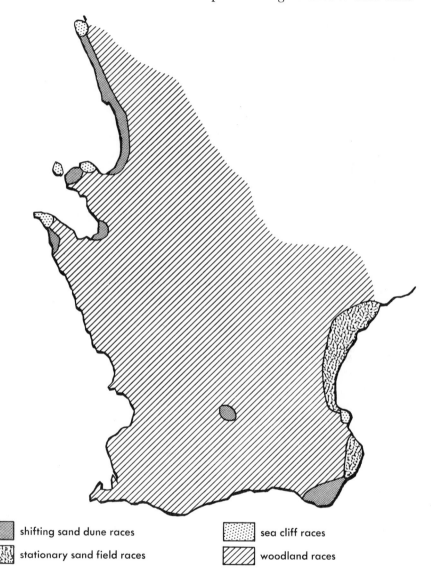

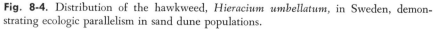

shifting sand dune races

sea cliff races

stationary sand field races

woodland races

Fig. 8-4. Distribution of the hawkweed, *Hieracium umbellatum,* in Sweden, demonstrating ecologic parallelism in sand dune populations.

life, the populations in the various sand dune regions may be markedly different from one another.

In the above situations the pattern of demic variation exhibits marked correlation with environmental conditions; sudden and obvious changes in populational characteristics can be noted between ecologic regions. The distinctive areas occupied by each ecologic race are discrete and the areas occupied by intermediate demes are very narrow. In many other species, on the other hand, the distinctive characteristics of the demes form a continuous variational gradient correlated with environmental gradients. In such cases the changes from one deme to the next are so slight that no obvious break is apparent in the continuum of variation. An example is found in the populations of Pacific herring (*Clupea pallasi*) of the eastern Pacific Ocean, which differ from one another in vertebral number and number of fin rays. These characteristics form a continuous variation pattern from north to south along the coast of western North America. In Alaskan waters the populations of herring have high vertebral and fin ray counts (Fig. 8-5). Southward along the coast each succeeding population is made up of individuals with slightly fewer vertebrae and fin rays than the population just to the north. At the extreme southern limit of the range all individuals have fewer vertebrae and fin rays than any individuals in the far north. While the Alaskan and Californian populations differ markedly from one another in these features, a complete transition in vertebral and fin ray number is represented in intermediate populations. A gradual, as distinct from sudden, change of this kind is called a *character cline*. The extremes in the cline are distinctive, but a continuum of gradual change from population to population exists between them to the point that it is impossible to group the demes into separate races. Clinal variation is common among living organisms and is usually correlated with an ecological gradient. For example, the character clines in the Pacific herring are obviously correlated with the water temperature gradient running from Alaska (area of cold waters) down to southern California (area of warm waters).

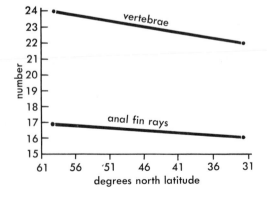

Fig. 8-5. Clinal variation in vertebral counts and fin ray number in the Pacific herring, *Clupea pallasi*, along coast of western North America.

ISOLATING MECHANISMS

While races and demes within a species retain basic genetic characteristics that make interbreeding possible when individuals come into contact, species are isolated gene pools. Some species are incapable of genetic exchange because of spatial separation. Others maintain their hereditary integrity, even when sympatric, through the operation of special isolating mechanisms that prevent interspecific interbreeding or reproduction. In most instances isolating mechanisms serve as external barriers to reproduction between breeding individuals of related species. In some cases crosses involving breeding between parents of two distinct species may occur and hybrid individuals with genetic characteristics of both parents survive to adulthood. In these relatively rare individuals the genetic contributions of the two parents appear to clash and tend to produce a number of internal barriers to genetic amalgamation that eliminate the hybrid from the breeding populations of both parental species. The various kinds of isolation between related species are indicated in the following outline:

A. Spatial isolation: allopatric populations

B. Genetic isolation: allopatric and sympatric populations

    1. Barriers between populations

        a. ecologic: prevention of mating

        b. ethologic: prevention of mating

        c. morphologic: prevention of mating

        d. physiologic: prevention of mating, fertilization,

           or development

        e. cytologic: prevention of fertilization or development

    2. Barriers in hybrids between populations

        a. hybrid nonviability or weakness

        b. hybrid failure to attain sexual maturity

        c. hybrid sterility

        d. hybrid nonviability or sterility in later generations

EXTERNAL BARRIERS (bracket spanning A through B.1.d)

INTERNAL BARRIERS (bracket spanning B.1.e through B.2.d)

Concrete examples of the operation of these barriers to genetic intermixing may be readily observed in numerous species. In the area around New Orleans, Louisiana, almost all of the different types of isolating mechanisms are seen to function among the various sympatric populations of frogs and toads. Each mechanism produces the same result, retention of basic genetic characteristics without contamination by gene combinations from other species.

Ecologic isolation is well illustrated by the pig frog (*Rana grylio*) and the gopher frog (*Rana areolata*). The former is extremely aquatic and occurs in deep ponds, lakes, and marshes among lily pads and emergent vegetation. The latter species occupies mammal and tortoise burrows during the day but is active at night around the margins of swampy areas. The pig frog breeds in deep water, and ecologic contact with the gopher frog is prevented since the latter breeds in isolated grassy ponds in shallow water. Differences in ecologic preference eliminate possible matings between the two species.

In many cases species with similar ecologic requirements breed at the same time and place but other isolating mechanisms prevent genetic mixing. Near New Orleans the closely allied gray tree-frog (*Hyla versicolor*) and pine woods tree-frog (*Hyla femoralis*) frequently breed in the same ponds. The principal barrier to interbreeding appears to be behavioral or ethologic. Female frogs and toads locate males by the calls given by the latter after they reach the breeding site. Although the gray tree-frog and the pine woods tree-frog are very similar in most characteristics, their male breeding calls are extremely different. In the gray tree-frog the call is a short trill, loud and resonant, of no more than three-seconds duration. The call of the pine woods tree-frog consists of a series of short sonorous dots and dashes. Female tree-frogs distinguish between these calls and no mixed matings occur.

Morphologic differences in size prevent hybridization between the oak toad (*Bufo quercicus*) and the Gulf Coast toad (*Bufo valliceps*). The oak toad is a minute amphibian attaining a maximum length of 1¼ inches in females. Small adult male Gulf Coast toads are 2¼ inches in length. Size alone prevents interbreeding since male oak toads are much too small to grasp female Gulf Coast toads and male Gulf Coast toads are so large that they are more likely to eat female oak toads than to try and breed with them. Even if courtship occurred between male Gulf Coast toads and female oak toads, the latter would drown under the weight of the former.

Physiologic isolation is represented by the relation between the leopard frog, *Rana pipiens*, and the bronze frog, *Rana clamitans*. The leopard frog begins breeding early in the year and deposits its eggs in a globular submerged mass near the water's edge. Bronze frog breeding begins in April and eggs are laid in a thin film at the surface of the water. The physiological control of the breeding season and egg deposition produces a barrier to mating and fertilization, respectively.

Internal barriers as isolating mechanisms have significance only after other restrictions on interspecies hybridization fail. Cytologic prevention of fertilization is the primary factor in failure of hybridization between the bronze frog and its close relative the bullfrog, *Rana catesbeiana*. Even when artificial crosses using sperm and egg preparations obtained in the laboratory are attempted, no development takes place. Obviously the chromosomes of the two species are incompatible and will not function properly to initiate development if brought into contact with one another. In other cases, although the genetic compositions of the parental species are antagonistic, development proceeds for some time in the hybrids. The resulting clash between the diverse genetic makeups frequently is delayed but leads to weakness or early death in the hybrid. For example, hybrids between the bullfrog and the gopher frog pass successfully through the early stages of development but die before reaching the tadpole stage.

Other hybrids attain adult characteristics but the chromosomal incompatibilities produce gonads that fail to develop properly and the hybrids are sterile. Hybrids between the Gulf Coast toad and Fowler's toad (*Bufo woodhousii*) are produced rather frequently under natural conditions. All individuals derived from crosses between females of the former species and males of the latter die early in development. Embryos produced by crosses between female Fowler's toads and male Gulf Coast toads develop normally into adults. The adults are all males and completely sterile. In many organisms hybrid nonviability or sterility do not make an appearance until the hybrid produces offspring by backcrossing to one of the parental species.

In this chapter we have sketched the basic outlines of populational diversity and isolation. The essential question posed by this outline centers on how the elementary evolutionary forces translate their effects into the origin of new populations. How does populational diversity arise? How do divergent populations become genetically isolated from one another? These questions have puzzled all students of evolution from Lamarck and Darwin to the present day. In the next chapter we will attempt to explain current ideas of the processes by which populational divergence develops within a species to form new demes and races and how the same processes operate upon the fragment populations until some of them become sufficiently isolated to form new species.

SUGGESTED READING LIST

MAYR, E., 1942. *Systematics and the origin of species.* New York: Columbia University Press.

STEBBINS, G. L., 1950. *Variation and evolution in plants.* New York: Columbia University Press.

WRIGHT, S., "Population structure in evolution," *Proceedings of the American Philosophical Society,* Vol. 93 (1949), pp. 471–478.

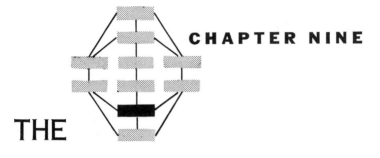

CHAPTER NINE

THE

ORIGINS

OF SPECIES

The entire course of evolution depends upon the origin of new populations that have greater adaptive efficiency than their ancestors. The study of populational divergence, or speciation, is therefore crucial to an understanding of evolution. At one time, and among some evolutionists even at present, the process of speciation was thought to be synonymous with evolution. As most biologists now realize, evolution is not a simple process involving only the origin of divergence. The factors responsible for race and species formation are considerably different from those operating to produce sequential microevolution, and evolution above the species level also entails a different complex of processes. Evidence has accumulated to the point where it is no longer proper to speak of a single origin of species, since we know that species may originate in several very different ways and under a variety of influences. The problem remains an intriguing one for all biologists, for we are far from fully comprehending the multiplicity of interacting factors that produce speciation in different groups of organisms.

DEME AND RACE FORMATION

The several patterns of random and nonrandom variation exhibited within species populations immediately suggest that the origin of divergence may be different under differing circumstances. The simplest conceivable situations leading to the formation of new populations from old are those in which a single deme becomes established in a new habitat. Imagine that a small breeding population of snails is introduced onto a moderate-sized island (one about the size of Long Island in New York). The population comes to inhabit a relatively small area near its point of introduction and after a few generations reaches genetic equilibrium. In what ways may new demes be formed from the initial population?

Obviously, new demes may arise in this situation only through migration and fragmentation. The original population will probably tend to expand and spread out from the center of introduction into surrounding areas. In the beginning, genic flow will continue between all portions of the expanding population, but gradually there will develop localized subpopulations in the most suitable habitats. When these subpopulations become partially isolated from one another, simply because the regions between suitable habitats are incapable ecologically of supporting snail populations for any considerable period of time, fragmentation has occurred. Each of the partially isolated demes may still retain the same genetic composition as the ancestral population, but the ecologic barriers to genetic exchanges between demes lay the groundwork for genetic divergence between them. Isolation, even if only spatial and partial, now becomes a decisive factor in evolutionary divergence. Without isolation the gene flow within the population precludes divergence, since no localized genetic changes may persist under the constant impact of recombination. Under these circumstances only sequential evolution takes place. With isolation, microevolution within the demes may produce markedly divergent populations. Isolation is therefore the key factor in the origin of new populations. Without it speciation is impossible.

To continue with the example of the insular snail, the possible results following initial fragmentation begin to relate to observed populational variation patterns. Let us assume that the entire island is now occupied by a series of demes, all of the same genetic composition and all partially isolated from one another. What forces will now operate to produce genetic differences between the demes? What are the determinants that will produce a pattern of random or nonrandom interspecific variation? And what extent will the conflicting forces of variation, drift, and selection play in producing evolutionary changes?

The fragmentation of the original population into a homogeneous series of demes is consistent with the known behavior of all living organisms. We have previously demonstrated that not all parts of an organism's environment are habitable and that demes usually become established only in small suitable portions of a particular species range. In addition, with the exception of a very few creatures—certain of the oceanic plankton, for example—no large homogeneous populations are ever found under natural conditions, since the population invariably tends to break up into demic units. Our example of a population composed of demes having the same genetic characteristics is theoretical for reasons given below, and if such a population did occur it would not remain homogeneous for any length of time. From the very earliest stages of demic fragmentation each segment of the population will be under slightly differing pressures of mutation, selection, and drift. If the fragment deme occurs in a small but suitable portion of the habitat the primary evolutionary forces will be modifying it from its moment of origin. Selection acting upon the variation within the deme may produce a trend toward higher levels of adaptive efficiency, or, if the population is small and selective pressure low, drift may result in fixation of striking nonadaptive features. Because each of the demes is partially isolated from one another, each may develop under its own particular combination of variation, selection, and drift, without great effect on adjacent demes or without being affected by them. Each deme proceeds along its own way by sequential evolution, virtually independent of other demes in the population. The principal bond between the demes remains occasional genic flow, which contributes to variation. Over a period of time each deme diverges from the others as a response to the impact of the evolutionary forces, but all of the demes are still bound together by a web of occasional genic flow. As long as genetic exchange is possible the demes retain fundamental similarities in common.

The general process described above may function to produce either of the two intraspecific variation patterns discussed in the previous chapter. If the impact of selection on variation is different in each deme's habitat, or if selection pressure is low but the populations are small, random populational variation results. The example of the klipfish (*Gibbonsia*) illustrates this point (Chapter 8). Each population within the species exhibits its own characteristic of body depth to body length ratio. Each deme appears to be undergoing independent microevolution with regard to this feature independently of the other demes. A random variation pattern is produced, since there has been a differential impact of selection and drift upon the genetic components of each deme. Frequently, selection pressure is moderately strong for certain adaptive genotypic combinations in ecologically different portions of a species range. Where this is the case, similar selection pressures may affect a considerable number of demes to the point that all of them will demonstrate the same adaptation. Nonrandom populational variation is the result, as indicated by race and cline formation in the western rattlesnake (Fig. 8-2) and the Pacific herring (Fig. 8-5), respectively. In these examples, large segments of the species population, including many demes, have developed a similarity in basic adaptive features under the impact of natural selection. Each deme within these species remains partially isolated, but demes under similar ecologic circumstances have attained a basic genetic similarity through selective pressures. The variation is nonrandom because it is directed by selection. Different segments of the population are adapted to differing environmental conditions within the species range.

Race formation follows two different pathways, depending upon historical factors. Many races and all clines are developed by changes occurring between segments of the species range continuously connected by modest but regular gene flow. In the example of the western rattlesnake, the Great Basin race (*lutosus*) and the populations adjacent to it (*oreganus*) probably developed from a once homogeneous population. Differentiation occurred as a response to differences in environments, as expressed in selection pressures. Nevertheless, contact through genetically intermediate demes (intergrading populations) is currently maintained, and differentiation appears to have proceeded even though the developing races were bound together by genetic flow. Under these circumstances, selective pressures on the two portions of the original population must have been extreme in order to produce significant changes. The two races are distinguished primarily by the obvious adaptive feature of coloration. The Great Basin form is a light-buff or drab-colored snake with small, dorsal, dark blotches and obscure lateral blotches. Its more widespread ally (*oreganus*) is a dark gray, dark olive, dark brown, or black reptile with large, dark, dorsal blotches and conspicuous lateral blotches (some montane individuals are almost completely black). These color-pattern characteristics appear to be correlated with soil color and composition in the two regions inhabited by these races, and appear to be adaptive in nature. In the zone of intergradation, intermediate populations occur on soils of intermediate color and are transitional in their color-pattern characteristics.

A second means of race formation involves the same principle of genetic change in a segment of the species population. In this situation, however, the populations undergo genetic differentiation during a period when fragments of an ancestral population were completely isolated (spatially) from one another. Allopatric race formation of this general type is relatively common and may be demonstrated by an example in which the populations currently retain complete spatial isolation. The population of spadefoot toads (*Scaphiopus holbrookii*) usually is regarded as made up of two races. One of these occurs in eastern North America from the Mississippi River eastward along the Gulf Coast-Atlantic Plain to Massachusetts, and northward to the Ohio River Valley. A second race occurs to the west of the Mississippi in Louisiana, east Texas, Oklahoma and western Arkansas. The two populations were apparently separated from one another by the formation of the Mississippi River bottom lands and are allopatric. Evolution has proceeded along independent lines in each of the separated segments of the population, so that at present they differ markedly in skull characters and correlated head proportions. Laboratory experiments demonstrate that the two forms are completely compatible in genetic makeup. Crosses between the populations produce viable and fertile hybrids. Isolation in this example is purely spatial and although two races have been produced through the differences in selection on the two allopatric populations, potential for complete genetic exchange is maintained.

On occasion, races that originally developed allopatrically come into spatial association with one another subsequent to differentiation. Frequently they have diverged to a point where some reproductive isolation or a reduction in genetic-flow potential has been established. Intergradation between these types of races is of limited extent, and many of the demes of one or the other race along the boundary of contact are apparently uncontaminated by gene flow from the other race. A classic example of secondary contact and intergradation is provided by the long-nosed snake (*Rhinocheilus lecontei*). Two races in the southwestern United States are involved in this problem. One race is found in the arid deserts of California, Nevada, and Arizona, while a second occurs primarily around the desert periphery in semiarid habitats (Fig. 9-1). The differences between the races are pronounced in scutellation and coloration. However, along the margins of contact between them a curious mixing of demes takes place. In this area some demes are typical of the desert race, others are typical of the desert periphery form, and still others exhibit mixing of genetic materials from both types. Occasional demes of the desert race are found well within the range of the desert-periphery form, completely surrounded by demes of the latter. The reverse condition also occurs. The two races involved in this example appear to have evolved allopatrically and subsequently come back into contact with one another after considerable differentiation occurred. Interbreeding is restricted as a result, but a moderate amount of genetic exchange takes place between the races.

Deme and race formation follow the same basic pattern. Before differentiation is possible, at least partial ecologic isolation must be established. When fragments of an original homogeneous ancestral population are isolated, effects of variation, natural selection, and genetic drift operate differentially upon the isolates to produce genetic divergence. Each population fragment tends to develop its own variation pattern as a response to the peculiar combination of evolutionary forces operating upon it. Races may be formed either as segments of a continuous population network undergoing different adaptive changes, or from completely allopatric portions of a previously connected ancestral population cut off from any genetic exchange by spatial isolation. Subsequently, a renewed contact may be established between the formerly isolated races, but there frequently tends to be some reproductive barrier between them and genetic exchanges are restricted.

Among the many unsolved problems associated with speciation, particularly at the demic and racial levels, are the relative roles played by natural selection and genetic drift in populational divergence. Both of these evolutionary forces tend to operate in the direction of reduced populational variability, but selection encourages adaptive genotypes, while drift may produce fixation in the population of neutral and nonadaptive gene combinations. For many years it was assumed by evolutionists and geneticists that all changes in gene frequencies within a population were in the direction of

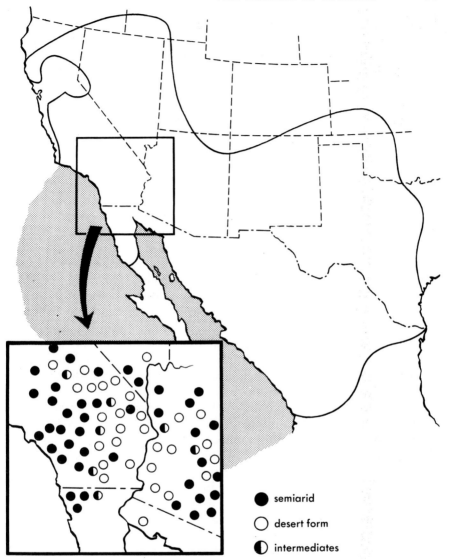

semiarid

desert form

intermediates

Fig. 9-1. Distribution of the semiarid and desert races of the long-nosed snake, *Rhinocheilus lecontei.*

greater adaptive efficiency. The concept of genetic drift was at first strongly resisted as being statistically possible but biologically improbable. Experimental evidence now supports the fundamental principle that small populations of a species—even if the environment is homogeneous, selection and mutation rates the same, and initial genotypic frequencies identical—will become differentiated over a period of time. The difficulty in applying this concept to natural populations is that the environments of each deme within species are slightly different, so that selection is also operative. The problem remains of determining if drift is an important factor in demic and racial diversification.

Perhaps if we re-examine some of the variation patterns considered above we may reach a tentative hypothesis regarding the relative significance of selection and drift in population formation. You will remember the example of the insular snails. At an early stage they had become fragmented into a number of isolated demes, each restricted to an ecologically suitable habitat. In our example these demes were originally identical in genetic composition. To simplify the model further, we will assume that they maintain identical mutation rates. Two possible influences may operate upon the individual demes to produce diversity. If the several microhabitats occupied by each deme are different in ecologic characteristics, natural selection will operate differentially upon each deme to produce gradual divergence. If no selective differences are functioning in the individual demic environments, genetic drift may produce divergence. Populations in which drift has been effective will usually exhibit a narrow range of variation in some nonadaptive feature that is fixed in the population. In addition, adjacent populations of snails will frequently exhibit striking differences where drift predominates. Since adjacent habitats of snail demes will usually be somewhat similar, there is a trend toward similarity in adaptive features among contiguous demes where natural selection is efficacious. Each demic population may then be characterized as a "selectee" or "drifter," depending upon the dominant force molding microevolution in the population. Re-examination of the examples discussed above will now give us some notion as to whether selectees or drifters are responsible for demic or racial formation.

In the case of the klipfish (*Gibbonsia*) cited as an example of random demic variation, it appears likely that the particular character analyzed has been fixed not by selection but drift. Each deme exhibits its own narrow range of variation in body depth to body length ratios, a characteristic not correlated with environmental differences. The general conclusion may be made that random demic variation is the result of a preponderance of drifters among the population units. Random demic variation is common in natural populations, and it may be concluded fairly that drifters are at full strength as components in species of this type.

Selection is the strongest element in most well-analyzed species exhibiting ecogeographic racial differentiation. In the western rattlesnake example, selectee populations apparently predominate over drifters, and contiguous demes under similar selective pressures come to form a network of demes with basic adaptations in common. This network of demes is a race.

Not all situations are as clear-cut as the two examples above. In the cases of the spadefoot toads and the long-nosed snake, it seems likely that the observed variation pattern is due to selection. However, many examples exist where small allopatric segments of a species population may be drifters, and other demes are selectees. An instance of this type is provided by the brown-shouldered lizard (*Uta stansburiana*). This reptile has a wide range in western North America and is composed of thousands of demes. In the Gulf of California region, isolated allopatric populations occur on a number of islands. The usual coloration of the mainland lizards is brownish with dark, dorsal markings and numerous light blue and bright orange or yellow flecks. One insular population on Isla San Pedro Martir in the northern Gulf is typified by all individuals being a uniform slate gray. Significantly, this island is hardly more than a small pile of boulders emergent from the surrounding sea, but the color of the rocks is precisely the same gray hue as characterizes the lizards. This small population has been under intensive predation by birds, and natural selection obviously has molded the genotypes in the direction of perfecting protective coloration. Another population on Isla Tortuga is typically represented by individuals that are a uniform black dorsally. This island is a volcanic cone covered by lava flows and volcanic rocks. Again selection has favored the acquisition of a coloration that resembles the black lava backgrounds upon which the lizards live.

Elsewhere in the Gulf, drifter populations of this animal have been established. On Isla San Pedro Nolasco, which is composed of light gray and whitish boulders, the lizards of this species are a bright copper green. They are extremely obvious on the light rocks and their coloration is nonadaptive to a high degree. Apparently drift has been the important influence here. Significantly, on Isla Santa Catalina, some distance to the southwest, another population of bright green lizards occurs. This island is a light-colored granitic ridge, and the lizards are again obvious and subject to easy predation by birds. Drift seems to be the only possible explanation of this situation, and since the Catalina population is rather distinct from the San Pedro form in other features, random fixation of the green coloration seems to have occurred on two different occasions in two different situations.

The conclusion to be drawn from this example is clear. In many species some populations are drifters and other selectees. Still others, we may assume, may be equally affected by the conflicting forces of drift and selection and might be called "neutralists" in the constant struggle for supremacy. That most species contain some demes of each of the three types is probably a valid statement. All three situations contribute to demic fragmentation and diversification, but in varying amounts depending upon the complex of conditions under which the species lives.

THE ORIGIN OF REPRODUCTIVE ISOLATION

You will recall from the discussion in the preceding chapter that speciation produces two distinctive patterns of genetic isolation between related species. In some cases the forms are allopatric and prevented from interbreeding by spatial isolation. In others the species are sympatric and are reproductively isolated by one to several isolating mechanisms. Theoretically, these patterns may have been produced in either of two ways, by allopatric speciation or by sympatric speciation (Fig. 9-2).

In allopatric speciation evolution may take place in two spatially isolated populations descended from a common ancestor. Differences in the interaction of variation, selection, and drift will operate in these fragments in exactly the same process of microevolution described for deme and race formation. If the populations remain separated for a long enough time, and if the interacting forces of evolution—particularly selection—operate to produce divergence, allopatric species are the result. Allopatric populations formerly separated by an ecological barrier that has been removed may come to share a portion of one another's range and become sympatric if reproductive isolation has been developed during the period of allopatry (see Chapter 8). Allopatric speciation follows microevolutionary pathways and is dependent primarily upon spatial isolation, time, and differences in environment, as expressed in selection, to produce new gene combinations.

Sympatric speciation may produce similar results. If new populations were to arise directly through the instantaneous appearance of reproductive isolation between segments of the same population, two reproductively isolated populations would result. If one or both populations moved out of the

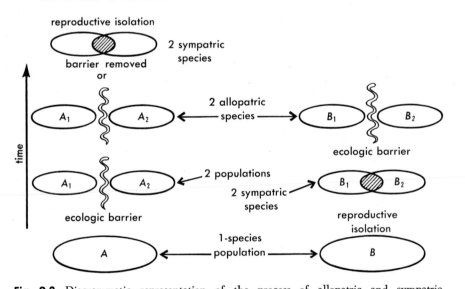

Fig. 9-2. Diagrammatic representation of the process of allopatric and sympatric speciation.

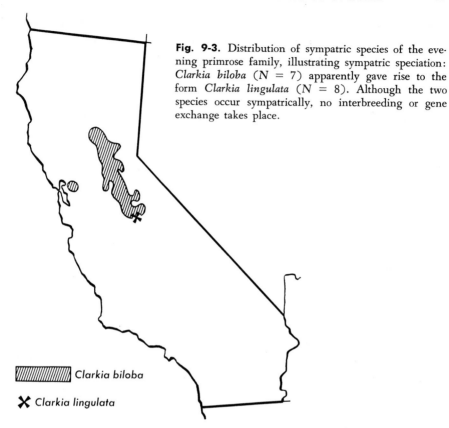

Fig. 9-3. Distribution of sympatric species of the evening primrose family, illustrating sympatric speciation: *Clarkia biloba* ($N = 7$) apparently gave rise to the form *Clarkia lingulata* ($N = 8$). Although the two species occur sympatrically, no interbreeding or gene exchange takes place.

Clarkia biloba

✗ Clarkia lingulata

original habitat, allopatric species would be produced. If the two populations remained in the same area, sympatric species would be recognized (Fig. 9-3). Once reproductive isolation is established, each population follows its own evolutionary course.

The process of allopatric speciation has long been recognized as a primary method of species origin. All evidence from the manner of deme and race formation and the frequent intermediate situations where originally allopatric populations, not yet fully isolated reproductively, have become sympatric (Fig. 9-1) substantiates the concept of allopatric speciation. Somewhat more controversial is the theory of sympatric speciation. Originally discounted as a primary factor in evolution, it has now become recognized as a powerful influence in species formation in higher plants. The process of allopatric speciation has been adequately covered in the section on deme and race formation, but further comment is required regarding the sympatric process.

Sympatric speciation may occur, at least among higher plants, in four principal ways: (1) by polyploidy or nondisjunction; (2) by hybridization between distinct species; (3) by self-fertilization; and (4) by apomixis. Polyploidy is a spontaneous increase in chromosome numbers that usually results in a new individual with 3N, 4N, 6N, or 8N chromosomes. Since polyploidy is usually caused by failure of proper meiosis, a number of offspring with a similar polyploidy may be produced by one set of seeds. Polyploid individuals are usually genetically isolated from the parental species. In the early years of divergence the diploid and polyploid species may occur together and be practically indistinguishable. However, once reproductive isolation is established, differences in gene combinations will result through microevolutionary forces. Nondisjunction is produced by faulty meiosis as well and acts to increase the number of chromosomes.

Because of the manner in which pollen is distributed, chance fertilization of one species by pollen from a closely related form is not uncommon in plants. Hybrid individuals frequently are produced. Sometimes the hybrids and their genes are reintroduced into the gene pools of one or both parental species by backcrossing to the parental types. Frequently the hybrids have faulty meiosis and produce hybrid polyploid offspring reproductively isolated from all other species. These polyploid species are now known to be very common. In the tarweeds (*Madia*), for example, the species *M. citrigracilis* ($N = 24$) apparently was produced through hybridization between *M. citrodora* ($N = 8$) and *M. gracilis* ($N = 16$).

The development of the habit of self-fertilization, an evolutionary shift by no means restricted to higher plants, may create reproductive isolation instantaneously. Unless cross-fertilization becomes re-established later, the course of evolution in each descendent stock is independent.

The sympatric origin of species by *apomixis* is also common among plants and many lower animals. Apomixis is a term applied to any asexual reproductive process that replaces the sexual method. A variety of apomictic reproductive types are known, but all produce offspring from unfertilized gametes or by vegetative means. When apomixis arises suddenly in an originally sexual population, the asexually reproducing individuals immediately form isolated gene pools. Genetic isolation is established and once again the descendent stocks evolve independently.

Unfortunately, what constitutes a gene pool or species in an asexual organism is a very real biological question. Groups of rigid self-fertilizers or apomictic reproducers are almost impossible to treat as species, since the offspring of each individual are genetically identical to the parent and reproductively isolated from all other individuals. Evolution in such forms is influenced much more strongly by mutation and drift than by selection. For convenience of discussion, and since most organisms are cross-fertilizing sexual reproducers, no further reference to restricted self-fertilizing and apomictic forms will be made in this book. The subject is a fascinating one and in need of a great deal of study.

The one essential problem in speciation, namely, the manner in which isolating mechanisms become established, remains unsolved. Evolutionists have proposed a number of solutions, but no single concept appears to be equally applicable to all cases, and most of the suggestions have not been rigorously tested. The mechanism of the origin of reproductive isolation between populations produced by sympatric speciation is relatively clear. Either the chromosome number or composition is incompatible for interbreeding (polyploidy and hybridization), or interbreeding ceases (self-fertilization and apomixis).

In allopatric speciation the following mechanisms have been suggested as leading to reproductive isolation:

1. If two populations are ecologically isolated for a long enough time, differentials in mutation, drift, and selection will ultimately lead to gene combinations that produce reproductive isolation.

2. If two formerly ecologically isolated populations become sympatric, selection will operate against any hybrids produced by accidental interbreeding and favor and reinforce all reproductive isolating mechanisms.

3. If the genetic controls of hybrid sterility are correlated with genetic features with a positive selection value, then genetic incompatibility will result from any crosses.

4. If sterility-producing genes are neutral or even nonadaptive, they may become fixed by genetic drift in small populations.

The question of how reproductive isolating mechanisms arise in allopatric populations and prevent interbreeding when the populations become sympatric still remains. Solution of this problem is one of the challenges in the study of modern biology.

SPECIATION AND ADAPTIVE RADIATION

Speciation may occur at a number of evolutionary levels. Divergent fragmentation of the species through ecologic isolation leads to microevolutionary change in each populational segment. New species may also arise through microevolutionary shifts in allopatric populations or by sympatric speciation followed by microevolution. Speciation may also involve a number of additional factors.

A classic example of speciation involving the interplay of complex forces leading to adaptive radiation at the species level is provided by Darwin's finches (*Geospiza*) of the Islas Encantadas (Galápagos Islands). Significantly, the study of these birds in their native habitat gave Darwin his first insight into evolutionary processes. The islands are located astride the equator, 500 miles west of the coast of South America (Fig. 9-4). The several closely related genera of finches found on the islands appear to have been

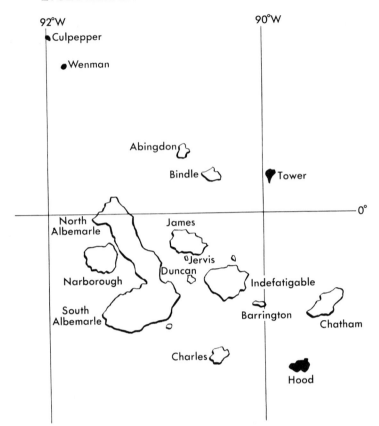

Fig. 9-4. The Islas Encantadas (Galápagos Islands). The islands discussed in the text are shaded dark.

derived from a single common ancestor. The group is distinctive and is not represented on the mainland.

The Galápagos are of volcanic origin and at their lower elevations are covered by scrub, thorny bushes, trees, and cacti. On most of the islands the upland areas are covered by humid woods. The ground finch (*Geospiza*) is represented in the islands by six species. Some members of the group are seed eaters and nest in a variety of low plants, others feed on the cactus fruits and nest in the cactus. Some species occur in the dry lowlands, others in the humid uplands. In the lowlands on the large central islands, three species occur, a large, a medium, and a small ground finch. A single species of cactus finch is also present. On the smaller peripheral islands the pattern is very different (Table 9-1). In a series of fragmented islands, allopatric speciation is probably responsible for evolution, particularly since these finches are very weak fliers. In addition, several of the insular populations of particular species differ from one another in essential characteristics. But the most significant feature of the distribution lies in the demonstration of speciation involving more than microevolution. What are the peculiarities of adaptive radiation in this example?

TABLE 9-1

Ecologic role	Central	Tower	Islands Wenmann	Culpepper	Hood
large ground finch	*magnirostris*	*magnirostris*	*magnirostris*	*conirostris*	*conirostris*
medium ground finch	*fortis*				
cactus ground finch	*scandens*	*conirostris*	*difficilis*	*difficilis*	*conirostris*
small ground finch	*fuliginosa*	*difficilis*	*difficilis*	*difficilis*	*fuliginosa*
humid ground finch	*difficilis*	.................No Humid Woods.......................			

First of all, note that where there is lack of ecologic competition, some species occupy several different habitats and fill several ecologic roles (*G. difficilis* on Culpepper). Where competition is present, the species have different ecologic relations on different islands (*G. difficilis* on Wenmann and Culpepper as compared to the same species on Tower or the central islands). Competition between sympatric populations has a significant effect in molding radiation. No competition favors generalized habits; marked competition leads to specialized ecologic roles.

A second force in radiation is ecologic accessibility. *G. difficilis* is blocked out from the small ground finch and cactus finch roles on the central islands (very likely it was forced out of them by other species competition), but where these ecologic situations are open, as on Wenmann, *difficilis* moved into them. Correlated with availability in radiation is the feature of multiple invasion of available adaptive zones. The cactus finch role has been assumed by three different species in the islands, and the multiple probing of divergent lines into similar adaptive relations is always typical of radiating evolution.

A final feature of adaptive macroevolution at the species level is provided by this example. Every pattern of adaptive radiation so far studied indicates a sequence of change involving the replacement of general adaptation by special adaptation through time. Failure of one species to compete successfully with another closely related form is usually due to the retention of a greater residue of general adaptation by the successful form. It is usual for a better generally adapted population arriving in a new environment to take the major portion of available ecologic roles, while the old resident population must become specially adapted. Examples are outlined in Fig. 9-5.

It is seen from the discussion in this chapter that microevolution and allopatric speciation at its simplest are essentially identical. Populational divergence is dependent upon reproductive isolation, although this isolation may be temporal between demes and races. New reproductively isolated species may arise through the interaction of ecologic isolation and differential microevolution. The origins of isolating mechanisms between originally allopatric populations remain a mystery. Sympatric speciation rests upon the establishment of reproductive isolation followed by differential microevolution.

The origins of species are diverse and are not simply the result of microevolution and isolation. In many groups the evolving species take on new

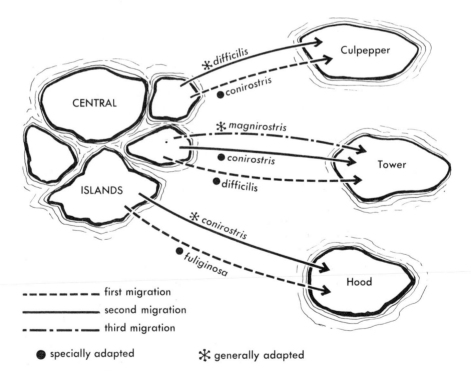

Fig. 9-5. Diagrammatic representation of the process of speciation involving the replacement of general adaptation by special adaptation.

adaptive relations of a high order involving major shifts in ecologic roles. Among the principal features of adaptive radiation in speciation are the interactions of interspecies competition, ecologic accessibility, multiple attempts at taking on the same new ecologic role by different populations, and the significant interplay of general and special adaptation. Evolutionary divergence at every level is a reflection of constant experimentation in innumerable directions and along a broad boundary of new organism-environment relations; its movement is driven by the elementary evolutionary forces, intensified by isolation, and modified by the characteristic features of adaptive radiation.

CHAPTER TEN

EVOLUTION
ABOVE THE
SPECIES

LEVEL
Our previous discussions have been centered around the forces and circumstances responsible for populational evolution. The effects of variation, drift, and selection on gene frequencies and gene combinations in sequential change or populational fragmentation have been our principal concern. Our attention is now directed toward consideration of the panorama of evolution, not in terms of the basic forces of populational change and divergence, but in terms of an understanding of the evolution of major groups of organisms.

The essential features of microevolution and speciation are now fairly well worked out by biologists, but the complex processes that lead to evolution on a grander scale remain an area inviting investigation. At the present time we have only the most shadowy impressions of the forces contributing to the adaptive radiation and diversification of life. For example, can the evolution and diversity of the flowering plants be explained simply on the basis of microevolutionary change, or are other forces contributing to macro- and megaevolution? The interaction of variation, selection, and drift and the taking on of new adaptive efficiency must play an exceedingly important part in these processes, but the grand pattern of evolution cannot be only the result of simple population change. The dim outlines of the course and general features of evolution above the species level are the subjects of this chapter. The history of major changes in life is well documented, in many cases by the fossil record, and glimpses of common patterns of evolution are provided by comparison between flowering plants and reptiles, corals and ferns, lungfish and horses. Nevertheless, the elucidation of the extremely complicated processes contributing to the development of major groups and new major general adaptations remains a challenge to all biologists.

THE EVOLUTION OF ADAPTATION

George Gaylord Simpson, for many years at New York's American Museum of Natural History, now at Harvard University, and the principal paleontological contributor to the synthetic theory of evolution, has developed a neat conceptual framework for describing major evolutionary patterns. We already know that at any moment in time the interactions of organisms and their environments define a series of broad or narrow adaptive fields or zones. All members of the same major group, for example the crustaceans, share one major adaptive zone because of their common posses-

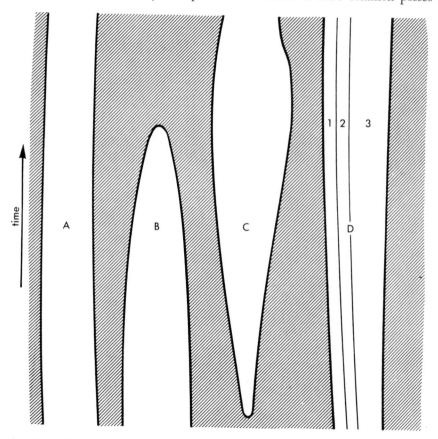

Fig. 10-1. The adaptive grid. Major adaptive zones are indicated by letters and subzones by arabic numbers; ecologically unstable zones are shaded.

sion of a complex of general adaptations. Within the broad zone each species of crustacean occupies a distinct but narrow field of its own because of the species' peculiar combination of special and general adaptations. Each kind of organism is an adaptive type discontinuous from other adaptive types; a crab is distinct from a barnacle (both are crustaceans), a snake from a man or a sunflower. Simpson suggests that for purposes of discussion the adaptive types or zones may be represented diagrammatically as bands or pathways on an adaptive grid (Fig. 10-1). The discontinuities between the major zones (A, B, C, D) are ecologic discontinuities or unstable ecologic zones. The adaptive zone itself is an ecologic role or characteristic relationship between organism and environment. Although the actual grid is of course very complex, with many subzones (1, 2, 3), a simplified form is satisfactory for our discussion. The diagram is extremely useful in attempting to describe adaptive evolutionary change.

Fig. 10-2. An adaptive grid diagram of evolution of terrestrial plants, indicating major breakthroughs and invasions of new adaptive zones.

The evolution of adaptation may be summarized in terms of the grid as follows: changes in adaptation involve movement of evolutionary lines within subdivisions of the subzones (microevolution), either from one major zone or subzone into others (macroevolution) or from one major set of zones into another (megaevolution).

The basic feature of evolution above the species level is the movement of a group of organisms into a new adaptive zone. In order to move across the zone of ecologic instability into the new adaptive zone, an organism must have evolutionary and ecologic access to it. In other words, the group must already have some characteristics adaptive to the new zone and the zone must be unoccupied by a strong competitor. An example is provided by the evolution of terrestrial plants (Fig. 10-2).

When a new major zone or group of zones is occupied, the first zone entered is usually widest and requires the least special adaptation. Later, more special zones will be occupied. The initial breakthrough to the new zone is due to general adaptation. Subsequent evolution leads to specialization. This pattern has been discussed in the macroevolutionary speciation of Darwin's finches in the previous chapter, and you might try to fit that example to the grid concept. We will return later to the grid as an aid in the explanation of other features of evolution above the species level.

EVOLUTIONARY TRENDS

Among the most significant features of macroevolution is a progressive, sustained tendency for certain characters to develop along an evolutionary line. Trends of this sort are numerous in the fossil record. Long-term continuing trends rarely appear in only one structure but almost always involve a complex of different features. Trends are of course produced by the driving force of natural selection operating within the limits of a particular adaptive zone or subzone. Evolution is not random, although certain elements in the process are random, and trends leading to greater adaptive efficiency are to be expected. Evolutionary trends are generally adaptive movements along one pathway, but they are never exclusively sequential and always involve divergent and repeated taking on of one or the other characters important in the trend. The populations undergoing change are constantly experimenting within the adaptive pathway, and parallel probings of a new subzone by related but different lines are the rule. In a sense, to refer to these patterns of divergent and multiple exploration of adaptive relations as trends is misleading, since a straight-line evolution of characters is not involved.

The classic example of evolutionary trends in macroevolution is provided by the horse family, Equidae. A summary of the evolutionary history of the

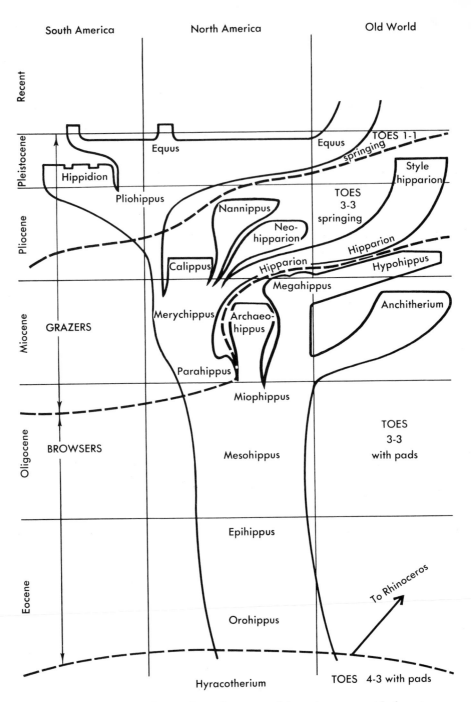

Fig. 10-3. Evolution in horses, from the ancestral browsing types with four toes on the front feet and three on the hind feet, padded as in dogs, to modern grazing forms with only one toe on both front and hind feet, hoofed and modified for springing action in running.

family is presented in Fig. 10-3. It will be seen at once that evolution from the small Eocene ancestor *Hyracotherium* to modern horses (*Equus*) was not along a straight line. Actually, the Eocene genus is almost as much a rhinoceros as it is a horse. The diagram is obviously greatly oversimplified, but it demonstrates very nicely the gradual change from a doglike, browsing creature, with padded feet, to a horse, with grazing habits and hoofed springing feet. This evolutionary history reaffirms the pattern of multiple divergences leading to special adaptation.

Natural selection provides the principal nonrandom force to evolutionary change, and apparent trends are due to the creative directive force of selection. Once a new adaptive zone is occupied, only a limited number of possibilities are open to the evolving stock. Each succeeding special adaptation limits the possibilities for future evolution. Attempts to fit the basic divergent pattern of evolutionary change into a rigid sequential scheme falsify the record and lead to erroneous conclusions. Trends in evolution exist, but they always involve multiple diverging trials within the adaptive zone.

ADAPTIVE RADIATION IN EVOLUTION

Macroevolution, or adaptive radiation, is a significant observable feature of change in all groups of organisms. Radiation as a factor in speciation has been considered in an earlier chapter and need not concern us here. Adaptive radiation above the species level is of greatest interest since the facts it supplies must form the basis for understanding the processes responsible for the grand pattern of evolutionary diversity. The evolution of the reptiles, which is one of the best-documented histories in the fossil record, will serve as a fine example of macroevolution and as a point of reference for its analysis.

The class Reptilia first appears in the fossil record in Pennsylvanian times (250 million years ago). Adaptive radiation in the group occurred between Permian and Cretaceous times, and living reptiles are derived from Cretaceous ancestors. The initial success of the reptiles stems from a megaevolutionary shift from aquatic to completely terrestrial development; reptile eggs, like bird eggs, do not need to be immersed in water to survive. The basic stock of reptiles were the Cotylosauria (stem reptiles), characterized by a primitive skull (Fig. 10-4). All other groups of reptiles are derived from this generally adapted group. Because of the major differences in skull type, each a modification to insure more efficient jaw musculature, and other changes, the reptiles are classified into six major subclasses (Fig. 10-5). Within each group adaptive radiation has occurred to produce a magnificent diversity of reptile species.

The basal stock of anapsid reptiles included the generalized order

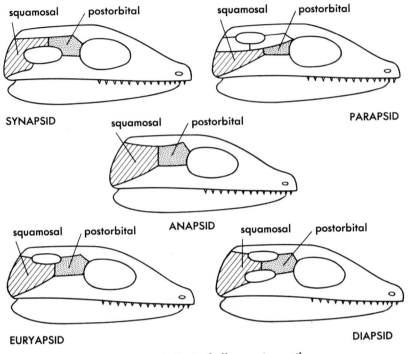

Fig. 10-4. Basic skull types in reptiles.

Cotylosauria (Pennsylvanian-Triassic) and the extremely specialized armored turtles, order Testudinata (Permian-Recent).

Derived from the anapsids was the ancient synapsid line, with three principal radiating groups. The oldest are the fin-backed pelycosaurs, order Pelycosauria (Pennsylvanian-Permian), and their less specialized relatives, the mammallike reptiles, order Theraspida. From the latter order developed man's ancestors, the mammals, sometime in the Cretaceous.

Also appearing early in reptile history were the aquatic members of the subclass Parapsida. Two orders, the Mesosauria (Pennsylvanian-Permian) and the fishlike Ichthyosauria (Triassic-Cretaceous), formed the group. The more generalized mesosaurs seem to have given rise to the specialized ichthyosaurs.

The subclass Euryapsida also showed aquatic tendencies. The primitive order Protosauria (Permian-Jurrasic) gave rise to the giant swimming pleisosaurs, order Sauropterygia (Triassic-Cretaceous).

The two largest groups involved in reptilian radiation are both characterized by a diapsid skull. The more primitive subclass, Lepidosauria, is represented by three orders, the basal Eosuchia (Permian-Triassic), the order Rhynchocephalia (Triassic-Recent), and the lizards and snakes, order Squamata (Jurassic-Recent). The tuatara of New Zealand is the lone surviving rhynchocephalian.

The second diapsid group, the subclass Archosauria or ruling reptiles, is descended from the lepidosaurian order Eosuchia. The basal archosaurian stock comprises the order Thecodontia (Permian-Triassic) and from it arose five divergent specialized orders of reptiles that came to dominate the terrestrial environment during Mesozoic times. Apparently the thecodonts represent a breakthrough into a new series of adaptive zones by taking on of a new general adaptation; four of the five orders of higher archosaurians differentiated through special adaptation while the fifth in its turn represents another major evolutionary shift founded on a new general adaptive type. Two of the thecodont derivatives, order Saurischia (Triassic-Cretaceous) and order Ornithischia (Triassic-Cretaceous), were enormously successful, with many families, hundreds of genera, and innumerable species. Members of the two groups are frequently called dinosaurs and included such diverse forms as small lizardlike reptiles, gigantic monsters, delicate bipedal species resembling flightless birds, and successful aquatic forms. None survived into the Cenozoic.

A third divergent line included the flying reptiles, order Pterosauria (Jurassic-Cretaceous). The ancestral line of this order probably were gliders, but the later forms were capable of flight.

The fourth line of special adaptation forms the aquatic order Crocodilia (Triassic-Recent), very successful in the past but today represented by only 21 species.

The fifth and final thecodont stock also took up the habit of gliding and then flying, and this habit, coordinated with the development of a new general adaptive complex of other features, led to occupation of the adaptive zone of aerial life. This group, the feathered reptiles or birds, has undergone its own extensive adaptive radiation to form the class Aves (Jurassic-Recent).

Certain features of adaptive radiation found in the evolution of reptiles are principal characteristics of macroevolution in all groups, from tree ferns and trilobites to seed plants and insects. These common elements provide the key to understanding the process of evolution above the species level.

1. All macroevolution always follows the acquisition of new general adaptation or entrance into a new adaptive zone. Darwin's finches radiated after an apparently generalized finch ancestor arrived to occupy the previously unoccupied Galápagos Islands. Reptiles radiated after completely terrestrial development was established as a general adaptation.

2. Macroevolution always involves evolutionary divergence. Macroevolution is not linear but radiating. Generally, radiation follows general adaptation and the invasion of a new adaptive zone through special adaptation in different divergent descendent lines. The radiation of archosaurian reptiles from the generalized thecodonts is a typical example.

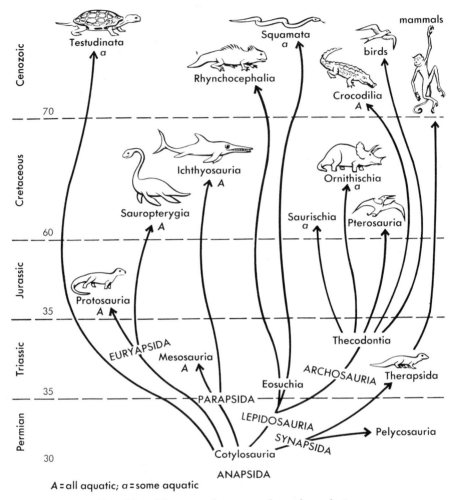

A = all aquatic; a = some aquatic

Fig. 10-5. The general pattern of reptile evolution.

3. Adaptive radiation tends to produce evolutionary lines that converge in special adaptation with other distantly related groups differing in their matrix of general adaptation. The ichthyosaurs show a marked evolutionary convergence with a number of fish groups in their body form, manner of locomotion, food habits (fishes), and free-swimming pelagic life. They are convergent in special adaptations but still share a group of general adaptations with all other reptiles.

4. Macroevolution produces groups of parallel special adaptations among divergent but related stocks sharing a common background of general adaptation. Among the reptiles, group after group has invaded adaptive zones in aquatic habitats. Representatives of every order except the cotylosaurs, the

synapsid orders, the eosuchians, rhynchocephalians, thecodonts, and flying reptiles have invaded the water and become completely aquatic. Repeated trials of the same general habitat or group of adaptive zones by divergent lines are always typical of adaptive radiation. A corollary of this principle is the feature of ecologic replacement in macroevolution. Where repeated evolutionary experiments with the same broad group of zones are involved, some groups arise, flower, and become extinct to be replaced by parallel groups that invade the same zone and undergo differentiation in their turn.

The phytosaurs (Triassic), of the order Thecodontia, and the crocodiles (order Crocodilia, Triassic-Recent) provide an example of both parallelism and ecologic replacement. The phytosaurs were very successful adaptations to aquatic life but as they became extinct the crocodiles, derived from a different group of thecodonts, replaced them (Fig. 10-6). The special aquatic adaptations shared by the two groups include location of eyes and nostrils dorsally, a large muscular tail used in locomotion, similar dentition for capture of aquatic prey, and devices for insuring respiration while nearly completely immersed in water. The specialized phytosaurs have been replaced by the specialized crocodiles and their allies, who in their turn are becoming extinct.

5. The basic rule of macroevolution is ultimate extinction. As general adaptation is replaced by special adaptation, groups become rigidly specialized to narrow adaptive subzones and are unable to move into new major zones. Since all adaptive zones must finally change and disappear, all groups locked into a narrow zone are doomed. Evolutionary progress consists of moving out of old zones into new ones through acquisition of new complexes of general adaptations. The fossil record is composed of the bones of extinct organisms that form the materials for study by evolutionists and at the same time offer immutable evidence of extinction as the ultimate fate of every line. Two reptile groups may be used to illustrate the reality of extinction. The order Rhynchocephalia was extremely successful up through the Cretaceous but is unknown as fossils in the last 75 million years. A single species, the tuatura, is a relict of the order and survives today in New Zealand. It is sometimes called a living fossil, although the term is a semantic absurdity. Relicts of a similar type are known in other groups and seem to survive through the retention of a modicum of general adaptation or as extremely specialized forms hanging on to existence by the thinnest margin. The extinction of the two dinosaur orders emphasizes again that evolutionary success through special adaptation is ephemeral. The road to extinction is paved with the remains of beautifully but specially adapted types. Final evolutionary victory over the malevolent environment requires progressive movement into new broad adaptive zones. Many lines never move out of the old zones; others fail in the attempt; but those that succeed form the advancing army of organic diversity and increasing general adaptive efficiency.

PHYTOSAUR

CROCODILE

Fig. 10-6. Comparison of phytosaurs and crocodiles: parallelism in evolution.

A common denominator runs through the entire picture of macroevolution, whether seen in Darwin's finches or the ruling reptiles. Every step in evolution involves the creation by natural selection of a vast array of adaptive experiments that occasionally break out of their present adaptive zones into new groups of zones. Every new breakthrough is dependent upon the breakthroughs previously achieved; an alga did not become a seed plant in a single step, fish did not develop directly into men. The adaptive shifts directly responsible for sunflowers or human beings were not possible without all the progressive evolutionary shifts that preceded them. The individual shifts depend upon opportunity, ecologic access, and the taking on of new general

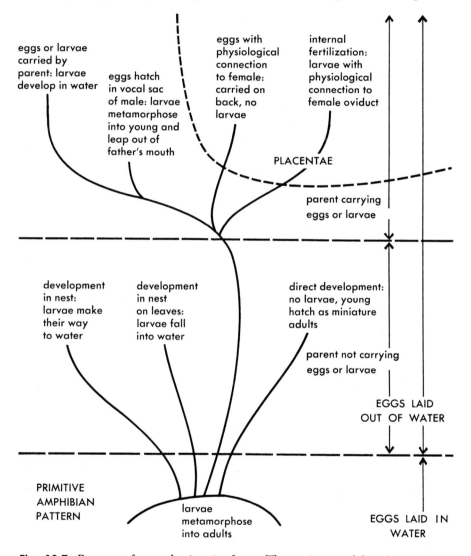

Fig. 10-7. Patterns of reproduction in frogs. The majority exhibit the primitive amphibian pattern. Each of the other situations has evolved independently in distantly related groups of frogs, except development in the oviduct, which has developed only once.

adaptation. The reptiles could not have evolved if amphibians had not previously invaded the land, birds and mammals are new permutations dependent upon the successful general adaptation of reptiles.

The adaptive experiments created by selection within an adaptive zone are of two types. Many are special adaptations taking their possessors into narrower and narrower subzones. Others, and these are at the base of any breakthrough to a new zone, are in the direction of the outermost limits of the present zone. Repeated attempts and combinations are apparently developed by selection until one line makes the breakthrough. An example of the constant divergent probing of the limits of an occupied zone by many different branches of the same line is provided in frogs by the many adaptations to reproduction out of the water (Fig. 10-7). Frog evolution in these cases parallels what must have been happening among Pennsylvanian amphibians as selection favored some kind of escape from aquatic development. One of the experiments took advantage of the opportunity and led to the reptiles. No frog has ever made the shift to a completely new adaptive zone, but if the opportunity arises, one of the probing lines may move across the no-frog land of ecologic instability into a new unoccupied major zone. The multiple attempts at crossing the barrier usually lead to extinction or failure, but at the foundation of every successful breakthrough a series of divergent testings of the unstable environment has taken place.

THE ORIGIN OF NEW BIOLOGICAL SYSTEMS

The central problem confronting all forms of life is the entrance into new major adaptive complexes of zones through development of new general adaptive types. The origin of new biological organizational plans, or megaevolution, is rare and shares features common to microevolution and macroevolution. The number of major general adaptive types developed during the history of life is small, but almost all of them persist without extinction, although a few have perished and others are relict. All of the phyla and most classes of microorganisms, plants and animals represent marvelously complex and coordinated groups of general adaptations each forming a basic, distinctive biological organization, unique and dominant in a broad range of characteristic adaptive zones. Fewer than 200 of these major biological organization plans have developed in 3 billion years. The origins of these systems are the most important of all evolutionary events; at the same time, the processes leading to these events remain the least studied of biological problems.

Megaevolution, insofar as the process has been analyzed, has the following clear-cut characteristics:

1. The breakthrough always follows evolutionary experimentation and

exploration by divergent lines of the ancestral stock, until one of them crosses the ecologic barrier into the new zone.

2. The breakthrough and shift are always rapid; otherwise they fail.

3. The new zone is always ecologically accessible, is devoid of competition, and requires a new general adaptive type for its invasion.

4. Adaptive radiation always follows the initial shift.

The origin of reptiles from amphibians demonstrates these several points:

1. Numerous divergent lines within the ancestral amphibians were taking on one or the other of primitive reptile characteristics in Pennsylvanian times.

2. The shift occurred over a relatively short period of geologic time.

3. The new zone, completely terrestrial life, was unoccupied, devoid of competition, and accessible since the ancestral amphibians spent only part of their life on land. The principal new general adaptations that made the invasion possible were development of an impermeable skin to prevent desiccation of the adults, and the land-laid egg that allowed the young to develop on land.

4. Adaptive radiation following the shift has already been covered in detail.

THE PROCESS OF EVOLUTION

The major feature of organic evolution is divergence guided by the molding force of natural selection. Evolution at the populational level is driven by the elemental forces of mutation, selection, and drift. In the short-term view populational evolution may be sequential, but it is always divergent in the end. Speciation, macroevolution, and megaevolution represent stages or levels in a continuum of evolution; all are driven by the elemental forces but are subject to increasingly complicated effects from other less understood forces as well. Selection becomes of greater and greater significance above the microevolutionary level.

Of greatest importance in speciation is the origin of isolation. Selection may act to produce divergence in this process whenever fragments of an originally interbreeding gene pool become spatially or reproductively isolated. New species are derived from old ones through the origin of reproductive isolation and independent microevolution.

Macroevolution and megaevolution are both incredibly complex in their dimensions. They involve in addition to the elementary forces and isolation the following characteristics, all related to natural selection and environmental relations:

1. The taking on of new general adaptation or occupancy of a new adaptive zone.

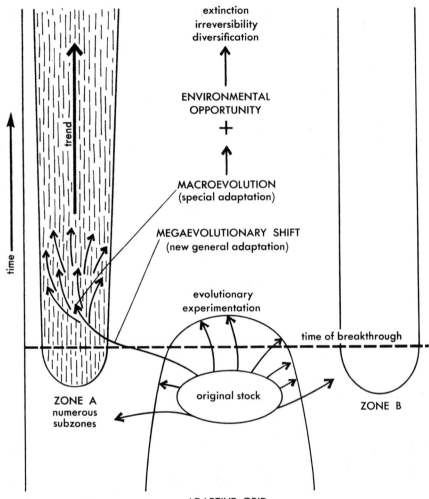

Fig. 10-8. The process of evolution above the species level: a diagrammatic representation of macroevolution and megaevolution.

    2. The breakthrough into new zones or subzones within the new adaptive zone by development of special adaptations.

    3. The loss of evolutionary flexibility, and channelization into greater and greater specialization within subzones.

    4. The ecologic reinvasion of a zone or subzone when it becomes partially unoccupied because its original occupiers are now specially adapted (ecologic replacement).

    5. The irreversibility of evolution. Since each step is dependent upon

the previous progressive changes, once a group is on the adaptive road, it is usually trapped in an adaptive zone and cannot reverse evolution against the direction of selection.

As an aid in thinking about the overwhelming complexity of evolution, these interactions are diagramed (Fig. 10.8) on an adaptive grid. In the words of George G. Simpson, quoted from *The Major Features of Evolution:* "In adaptive radiation and in every part of the whole, wonderful history of life, all the modes and all the factors of evolution are inextricably interwoven. The total process cannot be made simple, but it can be analyzed in part. It is not understood in all its appalling intricacy, but some understanding is in our grasp, and we may trust our own powers to obtain more."

SUGGESTED READING LIST

COLBERT, E. H., 1951. *The dinosaur book.* New York: American Museum of Natural History.

GOIN, C. J., 1960. *Amphibian pioneers of terrestrial breeding habits.* Annual Report of the Smithsonian Institution.

RENSCH, B., 1960. *Evolution above the species level.* New York: Columbia University Press.

SIMPSON, G. G., 1951. *Horses.* New York: Oxford University Press.

————, 1953. *The major features of evolution.* New York: Columbia University Press.

TAX, S. (ed.), 1960. *Evolution after Darwin: The evolution of life.* Chicago: University of Chicago Press.

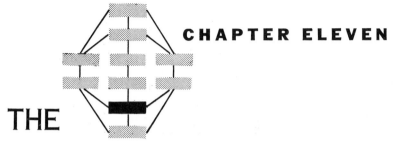

CHAPTER ELEVEN

THE

RISE

OF MAN
Among the most controversial aspects of Charles Darwin's ideas on evolution was his recognition that man was closely allied to other animals and appeared to have evolved from them. Although detailed fossil evidence was lacking, Darwin freely predicted on the basis of morphology and behavior that stages intermediate between apes and men would ultimately be discovered. During the century since the publication of *The Origin of Species* this concept has been repeatedly attacked on nonscientific and metaphysical grounds. Concurrently, however, fossil materials of apes, apemen, and men have been gathered from a wide variety of sources, and both the cumulative evidence and recent finds unequivocally support the theory of human origin from the higher apes.

Human evolution as seen in its basic outlines does not involve processes or mechanisms unique in the biotic world. In fact, compelling evidence for human evolution from other organisms is the fact that our historical development exhibits the same general patterns of linear and divergent evolution characteristic of all life. Man is, of course, a unique product of evolutionary forces and has attributes not found in other species; but so is every other species of living organism unique in its particular characteristics and evolutionary development. Human beings are interested in human evolution not because of any special evolutionary forces responsible for our origin and development, but because as one of our biological attributes as men we are egocentrically anthropomorphic. In some individuals our egocentrism is carried to the extreme in a complete denial of our biological relations and repeated statement that we are so peculiar that we cannot be the products of biological development and cannot be descended from other animals. Unfortunately, such statements are not based upon evaluation of the evidence but rather upon emotional or mystical grounds. As will be readily apparent in the discussion below, the crucial evidence of human evolution and the essential outlines of man's evolutionary progress are overwhelmingly convincing to all men with open minds. Those people who continue to insist that recognition of evolution from other animals somehow debases us or destroys in some unknown manner those biological attributes that have made us successful and unique evolutionary products, prefer to disregard the evidence.

It has long been recognized that man as a species is related to a rather diverse group of mammals, placed by modern biologists in the order Primates. This order is regarded as being among the more primitive groups of placental mammals and is characterized by retention of many generalized features that in more highly evolved mammal orders have taken on extreme specializations. The most significant structural features of the primates, and those to be expected in any proposed stock ancestral to man, are:

1. basically arboreal habits; some forms becoming terrestrial
2. limbs, hands, and feet adapted for arboreal existence, with opposable thumbs and big toes as modifications for grasping branches
3. vision and hearing the dominant special senses, with enlargement of appropriate areas of the brain for sensory reception from eyes and ears
4. concurrent enlargement of the frontal region of the skull to make room for expanded cerebral portions of the brain
5. generalized dentition and food habits

Living primates may be placed into two major groups and ten subgroups or families (Fig. 11-1):

I. Prosimii: primitive primates
Tupaiidae: tree shrews—tropical Asia
Lemuridae: lemurs—Madagascar
Daubentoniidae: aye-ayes—Madagascar
Lorisidae: lorises and galagos—tropical Africa and Asia
Tarsiidae: tarsiers—East Indies and Philippines

II. Anthropoidea: advanced primates
Cebidae: New World monkeys—tropical America
Callithricidae: marmosets—tropical America
Cercopithecidae: Old World monkeys—Africa and Asia
Pongidae: apes—tropical Africa and Asia
Hominidae: men—cosmopolitan

The course of evolution among the primates other than man may be sketched in broad outline on the basis of the structure of living forms and a fragmentary but convincing fossil record. The very earliest primates are closely allied to the generalized basal stock of placental mammals, a group called the insectivores. The insectivores are usually small, active creatures, and include among living forms the shrews, moles, and hedgehogs. The most primitive known primates were very similar to shrews in structure and re-

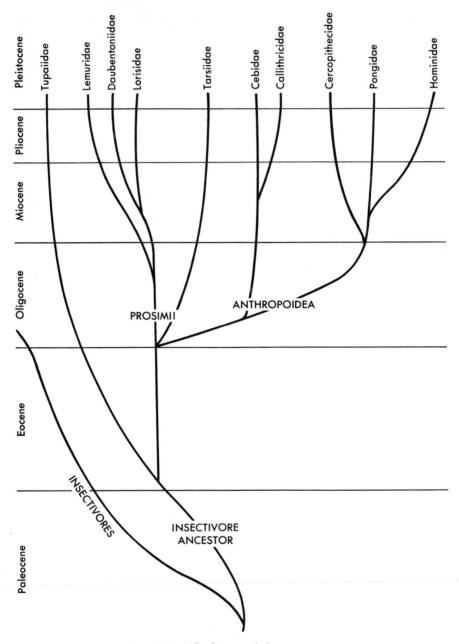

Fig. 11-1. The history of the primates.

sembled closely the living tree shrews. Fossil remains of these shrewlike mammals are known from the Paleocene, indicating the presence of primates about 70 million years ago.

More highly evolved members of the order, including fossil lemurs, tarsiers, and monkeys, have been recovered from Eocene deposits in both Eurasia and America. The first two groups appear to have originated from tree-shrew ancestors. Monkeys, in turn, seem to have been derived from rather generalized tarsiers, which lacked the specializations found in modern forms. Fossil materials from the Oligocene (40 million years ago) form convincing connecting links between the Old World monkeys and the apes. Apparently the most primitive apes were small monkey-sized animals. Numerous ape remains are known from Miocene and Pliocene times. Significantly, although they are definitely apelike in most regards, all these ancient apes exhibit few of the extreme specializations of the modern gibbon, orangutan, chimpanzee, or gorilla but have characteristics somewhat similar to those found in man. Modern great apes are more specialized than man in many respects, particularly in those features related to arboreal habits, and the fossil forms share with man the more generalized primitive conditions. Even though living apes are less humanlike in many ways than are their extinct primitive ancestors, it has been obvious to the majority of biologists for 200 years that men and apes are close allies. The rather recent finds of primitive fossil apes indicate an even closer affinity than was originally suspected. The similarities between men and the manlike or anthropoid apes have led to a general theory of a common ancestry of the two groups, a theory enhanced by the striking similarities between primitive fossil apes and the human species. It has been only recently, however, that the crucial fossil evidence of man's origin has been uncovered in a series of exciting discoveries in central and southern Africa.

The most important differences between apes and men are summarized below as a basis for evaluating the position of the newly discovered fossil primates so critical to our understanding of human origins (Fig. 11-2).

Apes	Man
1. cranium expanded; maximum brain size 600 cc	1. cranium greatly expanded; maximum brain size 1600 cc
2. occipital condyles posterior	2. occipital condyles anterior
3. strong nuchal crest	3. low nuchal crest
4. palate long	4. palate reduced
5. incisor and canine teeth large	5. incisor and canine teeth reduced
6. anterior premolar in lower jaw strong and pointed	6. anterior premolar in lower jaw small and bicuspid
7. pelvis narrow and elongated	7. pelvis broad and flattened
8. limited use and no manufacture of tools	8. extensive use and manufacture of tools

APE   MAN

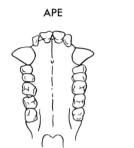

A

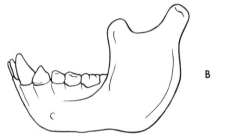
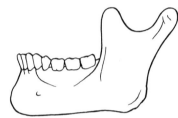

B

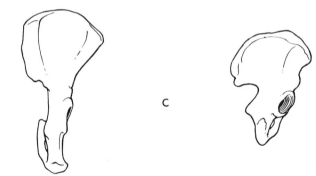

C

Fig. 11-2. A comparison of apes and men. A: roof of mouth; B: lower jaw; C: pelvis (lateral view).

Correlated with the expanded cranium and large brain size of man are his ability to reason, his fine memory, and his use of language, all of limited significance among the apes. The features of condyle location, nuchal crest development, and pelvic structure are associated with bipedal locomotion. The first two are related to the position of the head and its muscular supports in an upright stance; the last with support of the body and muscular attachments for the hind limbs in bipedal locomotion. Apes occasionally are bipedal, but normally walk on all fours when on the ground. The structural differences between apes and men in palatal and dental characteristics appear to show correlation with food habits. Man is more thoroughly omnivorous than the apes and is unable to kill animal prey with his inadequate teeth and jaws. Tool manipulation and construction in man are attributes made

AUSTRALOPITHECUS

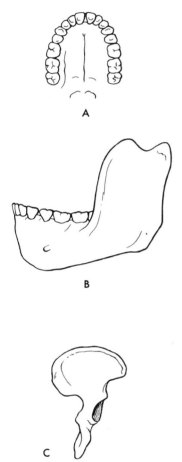

Fig. 11-3. The salient skeletal features of ape-men. A: roof of mouth; B: lower jaw; C: pelvis (lateral view).

possible by his upright stance that frees the fore limbs for uses other than locomotion and by the large brain centers devoted to manual control. These broad correlations between brain size, bipedalism, tool manipulation, and associated features suggest that the characteristics evolved more or less in conjunction with one another over a brief period of time. Strong positive selection for all the characteristics essential to man's dominance of his environment probably explains the rapid shift from ape to man during the last one million years.

Although the similarities in many features and the obvious relationship between apes and modern man supported the theory of common ancestry, the differences between the two groups in the essentials discussed above had still to be explained. Among biologists in the early part of the present century, these differences provided some basis for doubt as to the evolution of man from higher apes. Then a series of extremely important finds gradually filled in the gap between the two groups. The first of the critical discoveries of new fossil material was made by Professor Raymond Dart in Bechuanaland, South Africa, in 1925. Dart's animal, which he called Australopithecus (southern ape), consisted of a single skull that combined an unexpected number of human and ape characteristics. In succeeding years additional skulls, jaws, and other essential anatomical parts of Australopithecus and a number of other related forms were discovered in other areas of South Africa. These apelike forms are very similar to primitive apes in certain characteristics and like man in many others. The most ancient of these ape-men lived in early Pleistocene, about one million years ago, and some of them persisted until as recently as 400,000 years ago. Australopithecus and its allies share the following significant structural features (Fig. 11-3):

1. cranium expanded; brain size about 600 cc
2. occipital condyles anterior
3. nuchal crest reduced
4. palate reduced, but longer than in man
5. incisor and canine teeth reduced
6. anterior premolar in lower jaw small and bicuspid
7. pelvis broad and somewhat flattened

On the basis of these characteristics the ape-men of southern Africa agree with apes in cranial size and with man in the structure of the condyles, nuchal crest, and dentition. In the nature of the palate and pelvis the ape-men are intermediate between apes and man, but clearly tend toward the human condition. In addition, some evidence suggests that these primates used pebbles of various sorts for killing their animal prey, a condition bordering on tool utilization and a precursor to tool manufacture.

Interpretation of the preserved remains of the southern ape-men allows us to reconstruct their general features as compared to modern man (Fig. 11-4). The relatively small cranium and brain capacity indicate an order of intelligence lower than that of man but slightly higher than certain of the apes. The characters of condyle location, nuchal crest development, and pelvis are conclusive evidences of bipedal locomotion and upright posture. The palatal and dentitional conditions in the ape-men suggest that like man, Australopithecus and its relatives were omnivores incapable of killing large animal prey without tools. Although apelike in many ways, these small-brained, bipedal African pre-men are obviously allied more closely to man than to any other animal and form a connecting link between him and the apes. In most respects the ape-men resemble more closely the primitive fossil apes previously discussed than any of the living forms. Biologists are now in general agreement that the South African ape-men represent an early stage in human evolutionary differentiation and that Australopithecus and the other forms may be referred to the family Hominidae.

A recent discovery in central Africa reinforces the concept of human descent from the African ape-men. In 1959 Dr. L. S. B. Leakey and his wife found fragments of a fossil human skull in the remarkable Olduvai Gorge locale of Tanganyika. The site of the discovery is a deposit formed about 600,000 years ago. The fossil, named Zinjanthropus, is both an apelike form allied to Australopithecus, and an ape-man (Leakey prefers to call him a near-man) capable of making the crude stone tools with chipped jagged cutting edges that were found with the skull fragments. Apparently these crude instruments were used to kill and skin small animals. This exciting find confirms the position of the ape-men of Africa as human antecedents, linked to primitive apes but already manlike in locomotion, food habits, and tool-making propensities, at least in some forms.

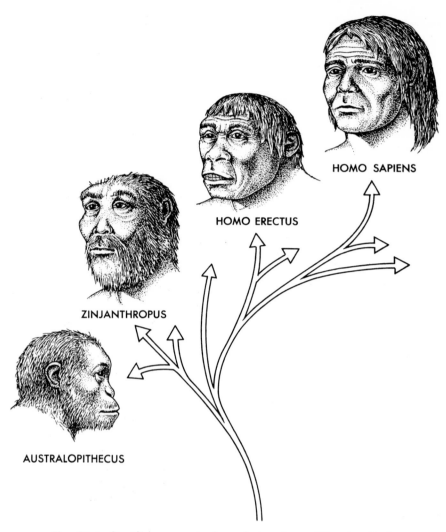

Fig. 11-4. Significant stages in the evolution of man (*Homo sapiens*).

Zinjanthropus is also important for several other reasons. The characteristics of the African near-man indicate that tool-making abilities appeared in human evolution before the tremendous enlargement of the brain and cranium typical of modern man, the species *Homo sapiens*. The brain of these tool-manufacturing forms was about as large as that in living chimpanzees (maximum about 600 cc), yet tool manipulation and manufacture occurred in this organism. Apparently, bipedalism freed the hands so that tool use and construction became evolutionary possibilities in the remote ancestors of man. Tool use first appeared, as far as is known, in primitive australopithecine ape-men about one million years ago and set the stage for the origin of tool manufacture in later forms, as exemplified in Zinjanthropus, several hundred-thousand years later or about 600,000 years ago. Once tool manufacture was established as an attribute of the human stock, an entirely new adaptive zone became open. Entrance into the new zone immediately created a situation where strong natural selection operated toward greater and greater levels of creativity in tool manipulation and design and in development of a larger and larger brain to expedite control and invention of tools. Correlated with the stimulus provided by tool manipulation and the increase in size of the brain areas for control of these and related activities was an increase in association centers in the brain. Very likely even in the small brains of Australopithecus the amount of brain tissue devoted to sensory and motor activity was different from that in the apes, and expansion of association centers was probably already initiated. The gradual dominance of association centers making possible speech, increasing memory, and allowing mental manipulation of complex and abstract symbols has given modern man unparalleled control of his environment and himself. As a matter of record, the principal progress in human evolution during the last 500,000 years has been in the development of a larger and more efficient brain, the expansion of tool production and design to extremely complex levels, and the conscious awareness and control by man of the environment through the interaction of mental and technological activities.

A disconcerting note has recently been added to the story of Zinjanthropus—and indeed to the whole history of man's evolution—by dating of rocks from the Olduvai Gorge site using a new technique involving potassium and argon rather than radioactive carbon. These tests indicate that the near-man lived around 1,750,000 years ago, but many students are skeptical of the validity of dates obtained by this method. There can be little question that the sequence of events described above for the transition from apes to apemen to near-men is essentially correct. If the new chronological data are valid, it seems probable that australopithecines were present at least two million years ago and the length of time available for human structural development was nearly double that usually assumed to have been involved.

A considerable number of fossil men are known to occur in more recent deposits than those of the Olduvai Gorge. However, the evidence is conclusive that australopithecines of the more primitive nontool-making types persisted up until about 400,000 years ago. Apparently ape-men, near-men, and true men (genus Homo) were undergoing contemporary evolution about 500,000 years ago. The former two groups are now extinct and only one of the several known species of Homo still persists, but it has become the dominant living mammal. Among the many significant features of Zinjanthropus is the fact that it combined certain features found to distinguish between later species of men. For example, certain skull characteristics link the near-man to the very primitive Java and Peking men (*Homo erectus*) that lived about 500,000 years ago. *Homo erectus* appears to have been an independent offshoot of human evolution not directly ancestral to subsequent men. Other species of Homo, including modern men, differ from the Java and Peking form in basic characters found elsewhere only in Zinjanthropus, additional evidence that the African near-man stands close to the stock of human origin.

Further comment is perhaps needed regarding *Homo erectus*. This species has been found in fossil deposits in China and the East Indies. No question exists as to its status as a man, since the species had an advanced tool-manufacturing industry, human morphology, and a society at least as complex as that of many of the more primitive contemporary human societies. The species differs from modern man primarily in skull and brain development. The cranial capacity has a maximum of 1300 cc and the skull is primitive in several features. Early remains of this form are of an age about equal to that of the latest known australopithecines. Human types basically similar to *Homo erectus* are known to have lived up until 200,000 years ago.

Several other species of Homo are known from scattered and fragmentary remains dating back at least 500,000 years ago. Members of the modern species *Homo sapiens,* to which all living men belong, first begin to appear in the fossil record about 100,000 years ago. Essentially modern men in terms of cranial characters are known from 35,000 years ago. It must be noted that the course of the evolution of modern man exhibits the same pattern of divergent evolution and extinction described in previous chapters for other organisms. Although frequently cited as an example of directed evolution, the fossil record of human history demonstrates that a number of diverse lines evolved in the general direction of modern man, without any sequence of replacement of one primitive form by a more advanced type.

The success of modern man is derived from his physical and biological inheritance from his arboreal primate ancestors. Most significant to later developments were the grasping hands (grasping feet were lost as an adaptation to bipedal, nonarboreal locomotion) used for arboreal locomotion, and the dependence on vision and hearing, with concurrent increased brain size. The grasping hands have made possible tool manipulation, and the large brain originally important in sensory reception and motor response has taken on new functions of even greater significance. Superimposed upon these fundamentals was the origin of bipedal locomotion, which freed the hands for tool utilization and construction, and the rapid increase in brain size, particularly in association centers. The shift from earliest ape-men to modern man in the short period of a million years amply certifies the selective advantages gained by these latter trends.

Of equal if not greater importance than the physical changes in the history of the human race are the myriad changes accomplished through our cultural evolution. The maximum acceleration of human evolution in its cultural phases has occurred during the last 5000 years, that is, during the latest 5 percent of the history of our species. Increase in mental ability, development of tool technology, and acquisition of speech have contributed to the rise of a complex sociocultural organization. Cultural evolution is nonbiological in the sense that it is independently inherited by each member of the culture regardless of his genetic origins. Each generation of mankind passes on to each succeeding generation information regarding the environment, social relations, and technology. In its earliest sense cultural evolution in human ancestors proceeded primarily by imitation. The habit of tool use was probably taught to each young australopithecine, and methods of tool construction were probably passed on by the same means among the higher australopithecines even in the absence of speech, although Dr. Leakey suspects that speech had been developed in Zinjanthropus. Acquisition of language and increased levels of mental efficiency accelerated the process of cultural inheritance, for now information could be passed on verbally and even the newest methods of technology could be taught to the new generation. Advanced technological developments and extremely rapid social evolution followed upon the invention of writing. Today men profit from the collected knowledge of thousands of generations of ancestors, with constant acceleration in improvement of techniques and ideas the result. Cultural evolution is of course a reflection of our biotic inheritance, since without large brains and free hands the results of our ancestors' experiences would be lost to us. However, this social inheritance of acquired knowledge proceeds at a rapid rate virtually independent of microevolutionary changes in human populations. The basis of human dominance of the earth is derived from our technical mastery of the environment and our cultural inheritance. Today we can look forward to a period of greater social advances by the large-brained, tool-making primate we know as man. In the not too distant future man may well have complete control of his earthly environment as the result of interaction between his biotic and cultural evolution, unless, of course, our cultural evolution in ideas and utilization of our mental capacities lag too far behind our technological progress. We stand on the verge of a magnificent era in human history; our principal problem for the future is in learning to control not the environment, but ourselves.

SUGGESTED READING LIST

CLARK, W. E. LeGros, 1954. *History of the primates,* 4th ed. London: British Museum. (University of Chicago, 1957.)

———, "The crucial evidence for human evolution," *Proceedings of the American Philosophical Society,* Vol. 103 (1959), pp. 159–172. Also *American Scientist,* Vol. 47 (1959), pp. 299–313.

DART, R. A., and CRAIG, D., 1959. *Adventures with the missing link.* New York: Harper & Row.

KORN, N., and SMITH, H. R., 1959. *Human evolution.* New York: Holt, Rinehart and Winston.

LEAKEY, L. S. B., 1960. "The origin of the genus *Homo.*" In *Evolution after Darwin: The evolution of man,* S. Tax (ed.). Chicago: University of Chicago Press.

———, "Finding the world's earliest man," *National Geographic,* September 1960, pp. 420–435.

———, "Exploring 1,750,000 years into man's past," *National Geographic,* September 1961.

Scientific American, "The human species," September 1960 (entire issue).

TAX, S. (ed.), 1960. *Evolution after Darwin: The evolution of man.* Chicago: University of Chicago Press.

INDEX